THE COSMIC GALLERY

THE COSMIC GALLERY

THE MOST BEAUTIFUL IMAGES OF THE UNIVERSE

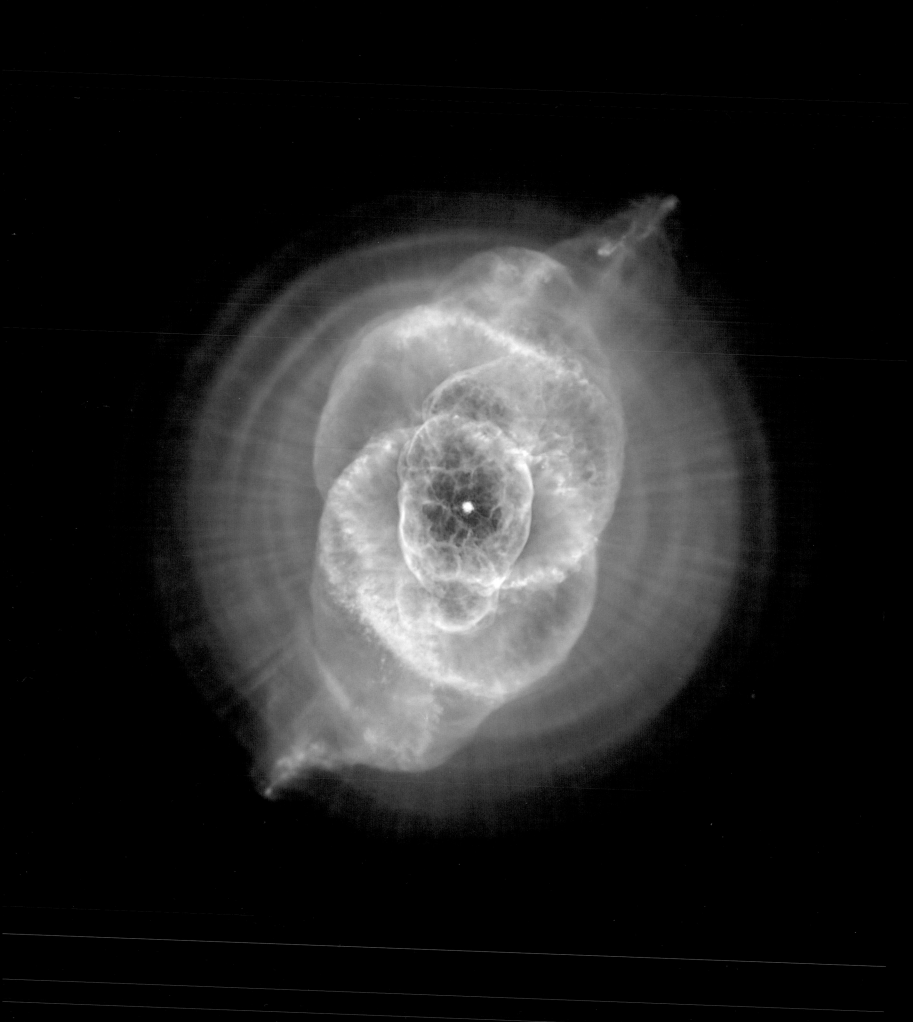

CONTENTS

IMAGING
THE INFINITE

Ever since the first stargazers turned their eyes to the heavens, humans seem to have had an urge to record what they saw in the night sky. Art and astronomy have been intimately linked for thousands of years, far back into prehistory. Telltale dots, some 15,000 years old, painted among the Ice Age animals on the walls of the famous Lascaux caves, appear to relate to star patterns we still recognize today. Meanwhile, under certain conditions, the rising Moon shines down the great passage tomb of Knowth, in Ireland's County Meath, to illuminate an ancient image of itself – the earliest known lunar map, carved into a 5,000-year old megalithic stone known as Orthostat 47.

By the dawn of recorded history, representations of the constellations, stars and planets are everywhere, ranging from more or less accurate, maps of the heavens, presumably intended for practical use, to more fanciful forms such as the

familiar figures of the zodiac (originating in ancient Mesopotamia and Egypt) and the planetary gods of the classical world. Later in the first millennium AD, Arab astronomers took the accuracy and beauty of their hand-drawn star maps to new heights, and medieval European scholars built on their achievements to create wonderful celestial spheres and charts.

But it was to be the dawn of telescopic astronomy that changed everything, transforming the sky from a single vast canvas for painting stories on a cosmic scale, to a mounting board for countless individual wonders, each of which could now be studied discretely and in far more detail. Galileo's first act, on viewing the satellites of Jupiter, the mountains of the Moon and the phases of Venus for the first time around 1609, was to record them in ink drawings that could ultimately be circulated to share his discoveries.

For the next four centuries, draughtsmanship became an essential part of the astronomer's skillset, the sketchbook almost as important as the telescope. Astronomical art rapidly developed its own vocabulary: since most were working rapidly with pencil and paper, sketching objects that rapidly drifted out of the eyepiece as the sky rotated through the night, it made sense to mark stars as black pencil-dots, and patchy areas of light as shade. To modern eyes, the results are irresistibly reminiscent of photographic negatives. Skilled engravers could later take such sketches and invert them to produce prints that gave a more familiar representation of the sky, but as often as not, astronomers knew how to interpret their colleagues' and rivals' recordings of the sky without such intermediaries.

As telescopes improved in both size and quality, they brought new celestial objects into view for the first time. The increased size of lenses or mirrors allowed them to sweep up far more of the precious light rays coming from distant parts of the cosmos than the human eye ever could alone, bringing fainter objects within view. Along with optical improvements it also led to increased resolution – the ability to divide narrowly separated objects and distinguish fine detail. A handful of nebulous objects and tight star clusters had been known since ancient times, but the 18th century saw their numbers grow rapidly.

From 1771, French astronomer Charles Messier made the first attempt to catalogue such objects – though in truth his prime concern was to avoid confusion with faint comets that he was more eager to find. Nevertheless, Messier's catalogue led astronomers to realize that there were several distinct types of nebulous object, some of which clearly resolved themselves into a multitude of stars under high magnifications, while others remained unresolvable – perhaps because they were truly gaseous, or perhaps simply because their stars were too numerous and far away.

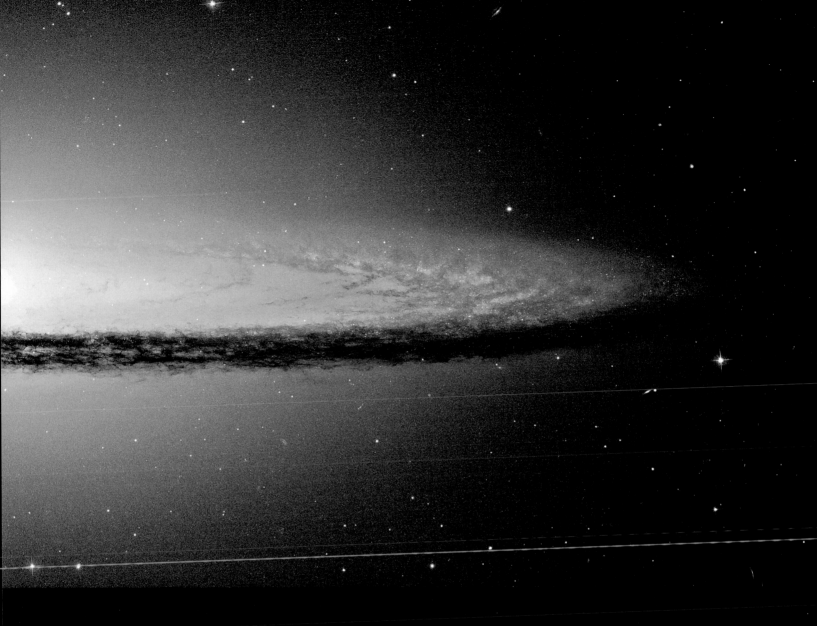

The art of the astronomical drawing reached its apogee in the mid-1800s, thanks largely to the work of one man. William Parsons, Third Earl of Rosse, was a member of the Irish nobility who used the family wealth to build the largest telescope of its time in the grounds of Birr Castle in Ireland's County Offlay. The 'Leviathan of Parsonstown', as it became known, was completed in 1845 and boasted a mirror with a 183-centimetre (72-in) diameter. It was only superseded, by the 2.5-metre (100-in) Hooker Telescope at California's Mount Wilson Observatory, in 1917. Parsons set out to revisit the nebulae catalogued by Messier and others, drawing them in exquisite detail and gaining new insights into their structure and true nature. In 1850, he published his researches at London's Royal Society, revealing that, for instance, that he had identified delicate spiral structures in several nebulae, and resolved others into stars for the first time. After Rosse's death Danish-Irish astronomer J.L.E. Dreyer put the Leviathan to good use from 1874–78 while compiling his New General Catalogue

of nebulae and star clusters. 'NGC' numbers are today applied to most reasonably bright non-stellar objects.

But even before Rosse had published his discoveries, new technology was threatening to revolutionize the science of astronomy. The first process for preserving images using light-sensitive chemicals was announced by French inventor Louis Daguerre in 1839, but even before then, he had used this technique to capture the first photographic view of the Moon. Daguerre's image was faint and fuzzy, but in 1840 US chemist and physician J.W. Draper repeated the experiment with much more success. Early photographic plates were famously slow to respond to light (Draper's image required a 20-minute exposure) and so the first 'astrophotographs' struggled to compete with normal eyesight, but they showed instant promise as a way of providing a permanent, objective record of the heavens. The technology developed rapidly, and an important breakthrough

came in 1863 when two Britons, William Allen Miller and William Huggins, used photography to capture and study the faint rainbow-like spectra produced by stars, paving the way for the study of their chemistry (see page 94). In 1883 British amateur astronomer Andrew Ainslie Common made another significant advance, using long-exposure photographs of the famous Orion Nebula (see page 96) to capture the light from previously undetected stars.

Today, photography is the medium by which we most commonly experience the heavens. The increasing size of telescopes and sensitivity of detectors (these days usually electronic CCDs rather than traditional film) has revealed unexpected wonders in the skies, ranging from the turbulent cloudscapes of Jupiter to the most distant galaxies, whose light may have taken billions of years to reach our instruments. Spaceprobes have sent back close-up views from across the solar system, showcasing the

beauty of space from the deeply shadowed craters of our own Moon's polar regions to the delicate play of light on the rings of Saturn. Images of our own planet floating in the vastness of space, meanwhile, have helped to spur awareness of our fragile environment.

Beyond the visible spectrum of light, orbiting observatories can now detect high and low-energy radiations such as X-rays, ultraviolet and the infrared, which are blocked out or swamped by our planet's atmosphere, while giant radio telescopes on Earth can view the sky in radiations for which evolution alone has simply left us unprepared.

And human ingenuity does not stop there – spaceprobes venturing out into the solar system are now routinely equipped with instruments to chart the surface of other planets in ways our ancestors could not have imagined, using radar to map

their geography, spectrometers to analyze their chemistry and magnetometers to identify the invisible force fields around them.

This book is in many ways a celebration of these amazing technological advances that have lately transformed our view of the Universe. And yet we should not forget that the images on these pages are just as much a product of human artistry as the cave paintings of Lascaux or the drawings of Lord Rosse. Not only are these technical achievements an art in their own right, but also the representation of data gathered by a giant telescope or a distant spaceprobe is still ultimately a matter of human choice. Many of the images shown here make use of false or representative colours to highlight certain wavelengths of light and particular structures, or to bring entire invisible worlds within the narrow limits of our perception. Others use unusual map projections to help us better understand the structure and geography of remote worlds. And still others use visual cues such as colour and tone as indicators of entirely different qualities such as surface topography or chemical make-up.

The result is the stunning variety of astronomical imagery, which often mirrors, or at least echoes, both traditional and modern art. The light we see rendered visible in many of these images has been caught up by our astronomical machines following a journey to Earth that may have lasted for thousands, millions, even billions of years. Other images are the product of robot spacecraft decades in planning and construction, arriving as whispered signals from remote parts of the solar system only to be swept up and amplified by the giant ears of radio telescope dishes. What we do with this information, and how we render and interpret it from bytes within a computer to the pages of this book, is unavoidably a human, and ultimately artistic, decision.

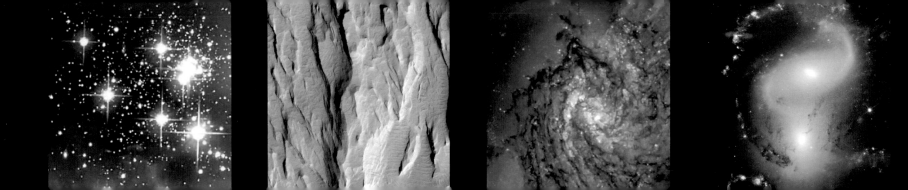

NEAR AND FAR 1

SOLAR ECLIPSE

The awe-inspiring spectacle of a total solar eclipse struck fear into the hearts of our ancestors, and remains an unnerving experience even today. As the silhouetted disc of our satellite, the Moon, creeps slowly across the face of the Sun – blotting out the comforting certainties of life-giving heat and light – it's easy to sympathize with the ancient Chinese, who believed eclipses were caused by a fearsome celestial dog or serpent engulfing the solar orb, or even with the Aztecs, who timed ritual sacrifices in order to placate the Sun god.

The total eclipse is a transient moment – an eerie interlude in which the darkness around the Sun contrasts strangely with daylight from the opposite side of the sky. The alignment of the Sun and Moon is so precise that the region of 'totality' covers only a small region on the surface of the Earth, sweeping out an 'eclipse track' around our planet as the Moon progresses along its orbit and the Earth rotates beneath it. For any one spot on Earth, totality typically lasts for just a few minutes. Nevertheless, astronomers have long since tamed these once unpredictable events. As early as 1504, the explorer Christopher Columbus was able to use his foreknowledge of an eclipse to awe the natives of Jamaica and save his troubled expedition. Today, enthusiasts chase eclipses around the world, seemingly addicted to this unworldly experience, resulting in stunning images such as the time-lapse photograph showcased here.

OBJECT **The Sun**

MEAN DISTANCE **149.6 million km (93 million miles)**

DIAMETER **1.392 million km (865,000 miles)**

OBSERVED WITH **Amateur equipment**

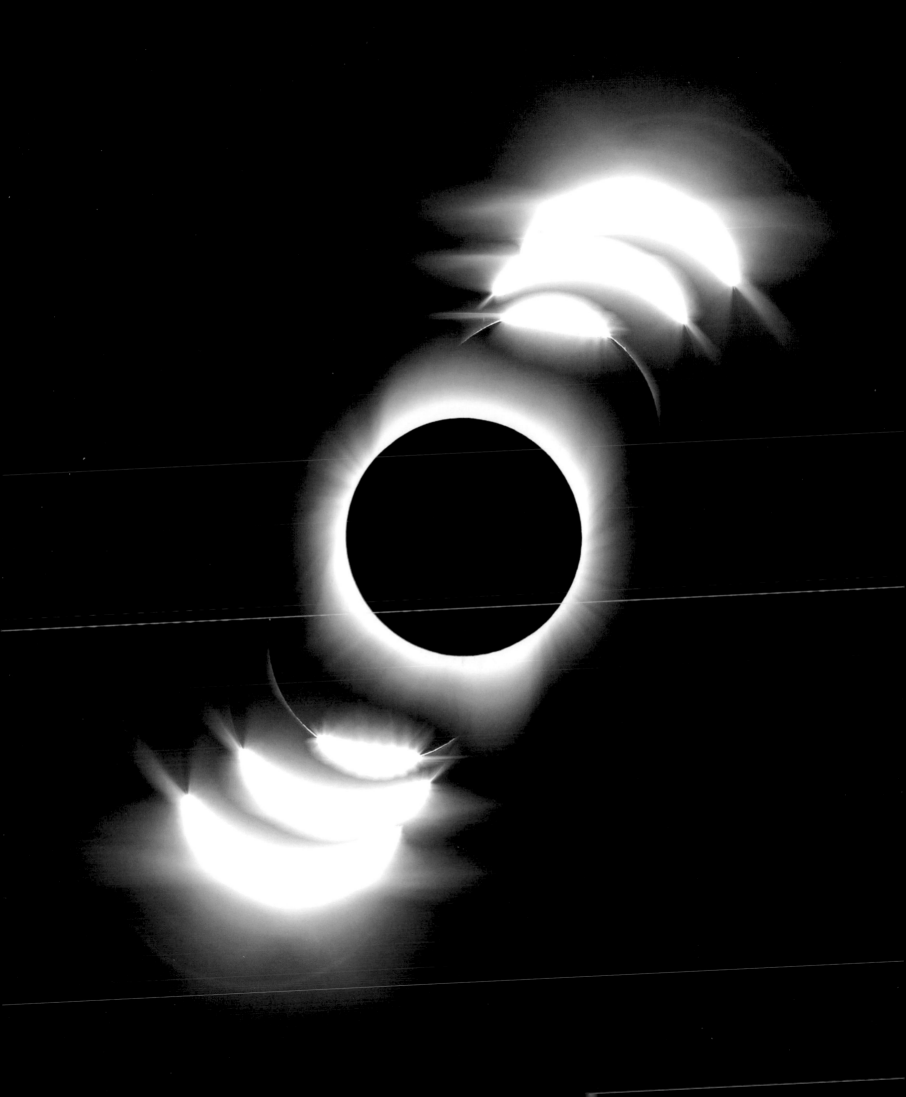

MULTICOLOURED
MERCURY

The cratered surface of the innermost planet comes alive with unexpected colour in this mosaic of images from the MESSENGER spaceprobe. During a 2008 fly-by, MESSENGER obtained the highest-resolution images yet obtained of the tiny, fast-moving world, photographing a strip of the equatorial region through 11 different colour filters. NASA scientists then combined the images, exaggerating the colour difference to produce this multi-hued montage of the searing landscape.

Orbiting the Sun in just 88 days, and spinning on its axis in 57, Mercury has a unique cycle of day and night in which most regions of the surface experience a sunrise just once every two Mercurial years. As a result, surface temperatures range from a furnace-hot 430°C (805°F) in daylight to a chilling -170°C (-225°F) in the middle of the long, long night. Fierce solar radiation and particles from the solar wind bombard the planet's surface, knocking off atoms in a process called spallation to form a tenuous atmospheric halo of oxygen, sodium and hydrogen. The same process slowly alters Mercury's surface chemistry, possibly giving rise to some of the planet's colour variations. Others are clearly due to geological processes or impacts from space.

OBJECT **Mercury**

MIN DISTANCE **77.3 million km (48 million miles)**

DIAMETER **4,879 km (3,032 miles)**

OBSERVED WITH **MESSENGER Mercury Dual Imaging System**

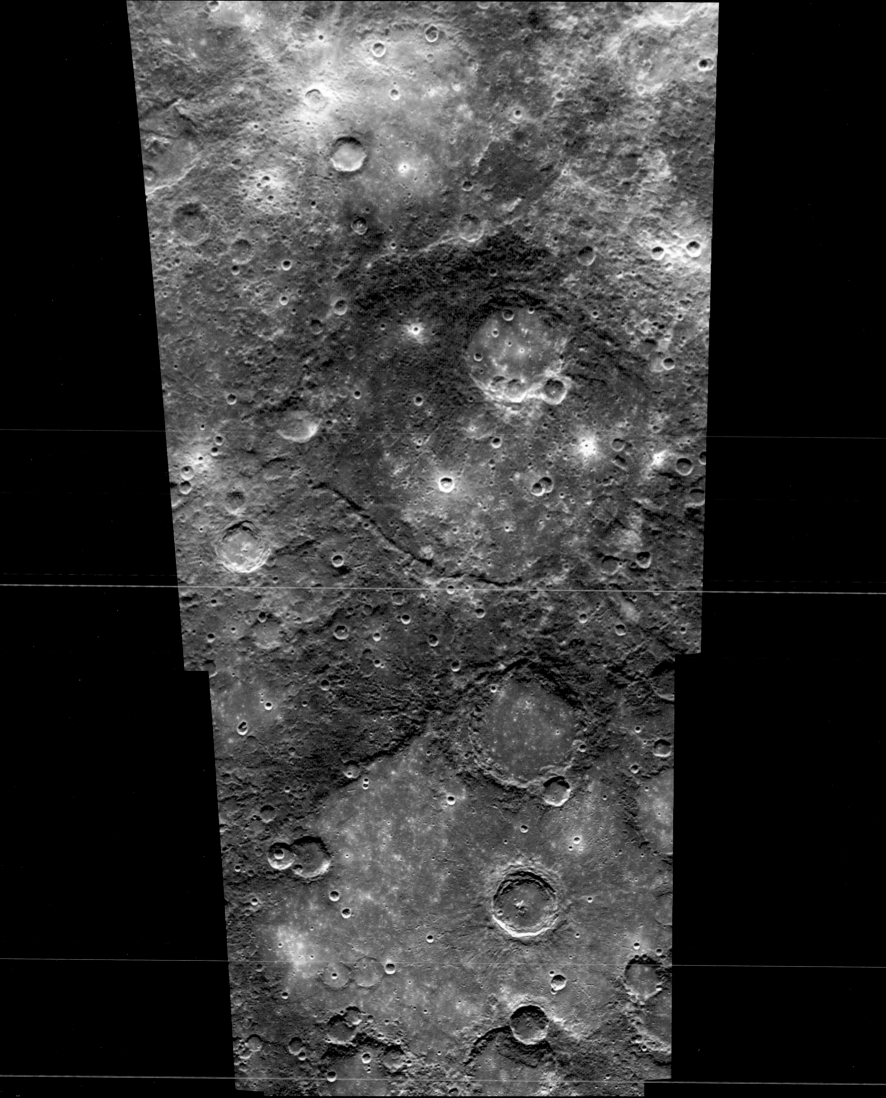

ALL THAT GLITTERS

A treasure chest of sparkling, jewel-like stars known as NGC 602 nestles within an Aladdin's cave of surrounding nebulosity in the Small Magellanic Cloud, a satellite galaxy of the Milky Way around 200,000 light years from Earth. As radiation and stellar winds from the newborn stars at its centre force back the clouds of gas and dust that gave birth to them, they sculpt enormous billowing sheets tens of light years across. The resulting nebula is known as N90. The densest regions of this cloud – probable sites of ongoing star formation – cling on against these forces of erosion, producing dark pillars and tendrils that form stalactites and stalagmites studding the cavern's interior. Meanwhile, as ultraviolet light from the central stars bombards the inner surface of the cloud, the cavern's interior is filled with a haze of glowing, excited gas.

The stunning composition of this Hubble Space Telescope image helps to bring home the three-dimensional nature of the night sky and the Universe in which we live. Not only does the central cluster illuminate the structure of the surrounding cavern, but in places, light shines through from far more distant objects – galaxies that may lie tens, even hundreds of millions of light years beyond this relatively close galactic neighbour.

OBJECT **NGC 602, N90**

DISTANCE **196,000 light years**

RA **01h 29m 31s**

DEC **-73° 33' 15"**

OBSERVED WITH **Hubble Space Telescope**
Advanced Camera for Surveys

RING NEBULA

The famous circular nebula of the constellation Lyra, catalogued as Messier 57, forms a limpid pool of blue fringed by outer shores of red and yellow in this beautiful Hubble Space Telescope image. Although assembled from three monochrome images taken at different wavelengths, the end result accurately mimics the colours we would see within this circle of light if our eyes were sensitive enough. The sheen of blue light around the central star emanates from superhot helium atoms, while green is produced by oxygen atoms, transformed into electrically charged ions by fierce radiation from the star. Red light, meanwhile, shows the presence of nitrogen in the nebula's outermost visible layers, and infrared images can trace ripples of gas far beyond the visible boundaries.

The Ring Nebula is the prototype for the class of objects named planetary nebulae for their passing resemblance to faint, ghostly planets in the telescopes of their 18th-century discoverers. They are now understood to mark the death throes of swollen red giant stars (the penultimate stage of evolution for stars like our own Sun). As a red giant becomes unstable, it undergoes a series of violent expansions and contractions, flinging off its outer layers into surrounding space, while exposing its hotter interior to view for the first time. While the Ring appears perfectly spherical or circular, it is in fact 'bipolar' – a double-lobed, hourglass-like structure more than a light year wide, which just happens to be aligned perfectly towards Earth.

OBJECT **Ring Nebula, M57**

DISTANCE **1,500 light years**

RA **18h 53m 35s**

DEC **+33° 01' 45"**

OBSERVED WITH **Hubble Space Telescope**
Wide Field and Planetary Camera 2

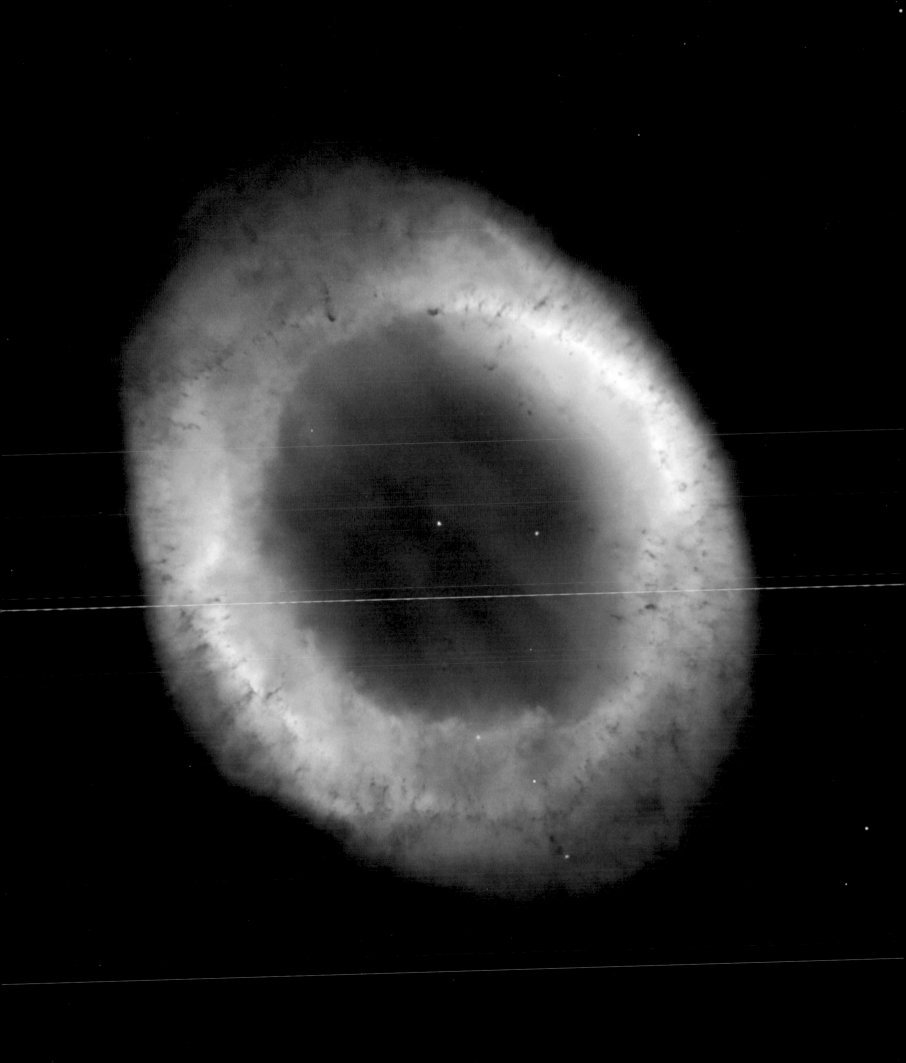

LAKES OF TITAN

A computer projection of the north polar region of Saturn's giant moon Titan reveals interlocking strips of landscape mapped by the microwave radar instrument aboard the Cassini spaceprobe. Saturn's largest moon – the second largest satellite in the solar system after Jupiter's giant Ganymede – is cloaked in an opaque, methane-rich atmosphere that normally hides its surface from view, but Cassini's instruments are able to map swathes of the surface as the spaceprobe flies past on its convoluted, looping orbit around Saturn. The artificial colouring of the surface is based on a handful of images sent back from the Huygens Titan lander during its 2005 descent through the clouds, while dark blue areas show regions of unusual smoothness and radar absorption – lakes filled with liquid hydrocarbon chemicals such as ethane and methane. The largest of these, such as Ligeia Mare at upper right, are comparable in size to North America's Great Lakes.

The existence of lakes on Titan has been suspected ever since the nature of its atmosphere became clear in the early 1980s. Scientists speculated that, at temperatures of around -179°C (-290°F), methane plays a similar role to water on Earth, transforming between solid, liquid and vapour phases and sculpting an eroded landscape that bears a sometimes uncanny resemblance to Earth's own. However, Titan's lakes seem to be largely concentrated around the moon's poles, while the equatorial regions, where the Huygens lander descended, appear to be much drier.

OBJECT **Titan**

SATELLITE OF **Saturn**

MIN DISTANCE **1.2 billion km (750 million miles)**

DIAMETER **5,152 km (3,201 miles)**

OBSERVED WITH **Cassini RADAR Instrument**

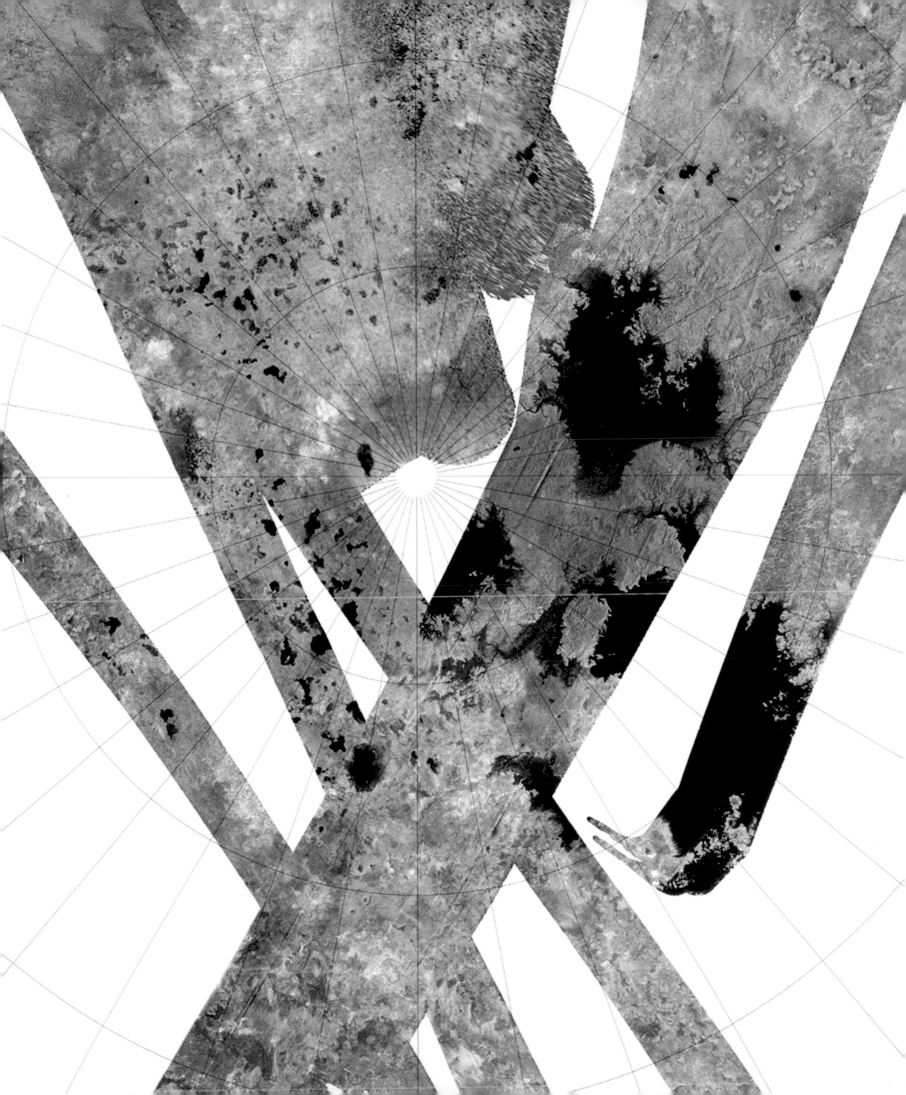

ON THE EDGE

A ragged line of red and black resembles a trail of glowing embers, strewn along the length of this edge-on spiral galaxy some 85 million light years from Earth. Galaxy NGC 5775, in the constellation of Virgo, is in the midst of a starburst – a period of massively accelerated starbirth triggered by a close encounter with the nearby galaxy NGC 5774. Great chains of star-forming nebulae have ignited among the dark clouds of dust and gas that encircle the galaxy, while the central disc, seen at only a shallow angle, glows with unusual intensity. In this Hubble Space Telescope view, a red-filtered image of the galaxy's visible light has been tinted blue, while light specifically emitted by hydrogen-rich nebulae is shown in red in order to highlight regions of active star formation.

Although edge-on galaxies such as this one frustrate efforts to see their detailed structure, they do offer astronomers a unique perspective that can reveal other features. All spirals are surrounded by a roughly spherical halo that extends above and below the disc. Dense globular clusters and rogue 'halo stars' are often found in this region, but in interacting galaxies such as NGC 5775, the region is also filled with hot gas, emitting X-rays at temperatures of hundreds of thousands of degrees. The origin of this gas is still uncertain, but many astronomers believe it comes from frequent supernova explosions marking the deaths of massive stars in the galactic disc.

OBJECT **NGC 5775**

DISTANCE **85 million light years**

RA **14h 53m 58s**

DEC **+03° 32' 40"**

OBSERVED WITH **Hubble Space Telescope**

Advanced Camera for Surveys

FLAME NEBULA

Light blossoms at the heart of a cloud of gas in Orion, illuminating multilayered sheets of interstellar material and silhouetting a column of dust studded with newborn stars. In visible light, the central regions of this impressive nebula, known as NGC 2024 or the Flame, are hidden from view behind dark dust lanes that sculpt it into tongues of fire. However, this near-infrared view from the European Southern Observatory's VISTA instrument transforms the flame into a flower, rendering much of the intervening material transparent. The remaining dark core is surrounded by young stars, recently formed at its heart. Stellar winds from these newborn stars blow out through the nebula, plucking at the surrounding layers of gas to create rippled sheets.

The Flame lies close to Alnitak, a hot blue-white star in Orion's Belt. As ultraviolet radiation from Alnitak rains down on the hydrogen clouds of the Flame, it splits the gas into electrically charged ions and electrons. As the ions recombine, they release excess energy at visible and infrared wavelengths to create the glowing fires of the Flame.

OBJECT **Flame Nebula, NGC 2024**

DISTANCE **1,500 light years**

RA **05h 41m 54s**

DEC **-1° 51' 00"**

OBSERVED WITH

European Southern Observatory

Visible and Infrared Survey

Telescope for Astronomy

➤ OPPOSITE

MARS IN STRIPS

Four separate images, collected by NASA's Mars Reconnaissance Orbiter (MRO), form a striking geometrical composition that reveals the variety of Martian surface features. Since entering orbit around the Red Planet in 2006, MRO has been photographing the Martian surface in unprecedented detail, one elongated strip at a time.

MRO's primary instrument is HiRISE, the High-Resolution Imaging Science Experiment. This powerful camera uses a reflecting telescope with a 50-centimetre (20-in) aperture to direct images of the surface onto a row of 14 electronic CCD detectors. From the spaceprobe's average altitude of 300 kilometres (186 miles), it resolves details up to 0.3 metres (1 ft) across, allowing it to see, for example, robot rovers on the Martian surface, and a host of natural features. The images collected here show (from top to bottom) the region surrounding Kaiser Crater in the southern Martian highlands, shattered rock fragments around a canyon called Nili Fossae, sand dunes forming around an equatorial rock formation and an eroded impact crater known as Aram Chaos.

OBJECT **Mars**

MIN DISTANCE **54.6 million km**
(33.9 million miles)

DIAMETER **6,792 km (4,220 miles)**

OBSERVED WITH

Mars Reconnaissance Orbiter

High-Resolution Imaging

Science Experiment

➤ ➤ OVERLEAF

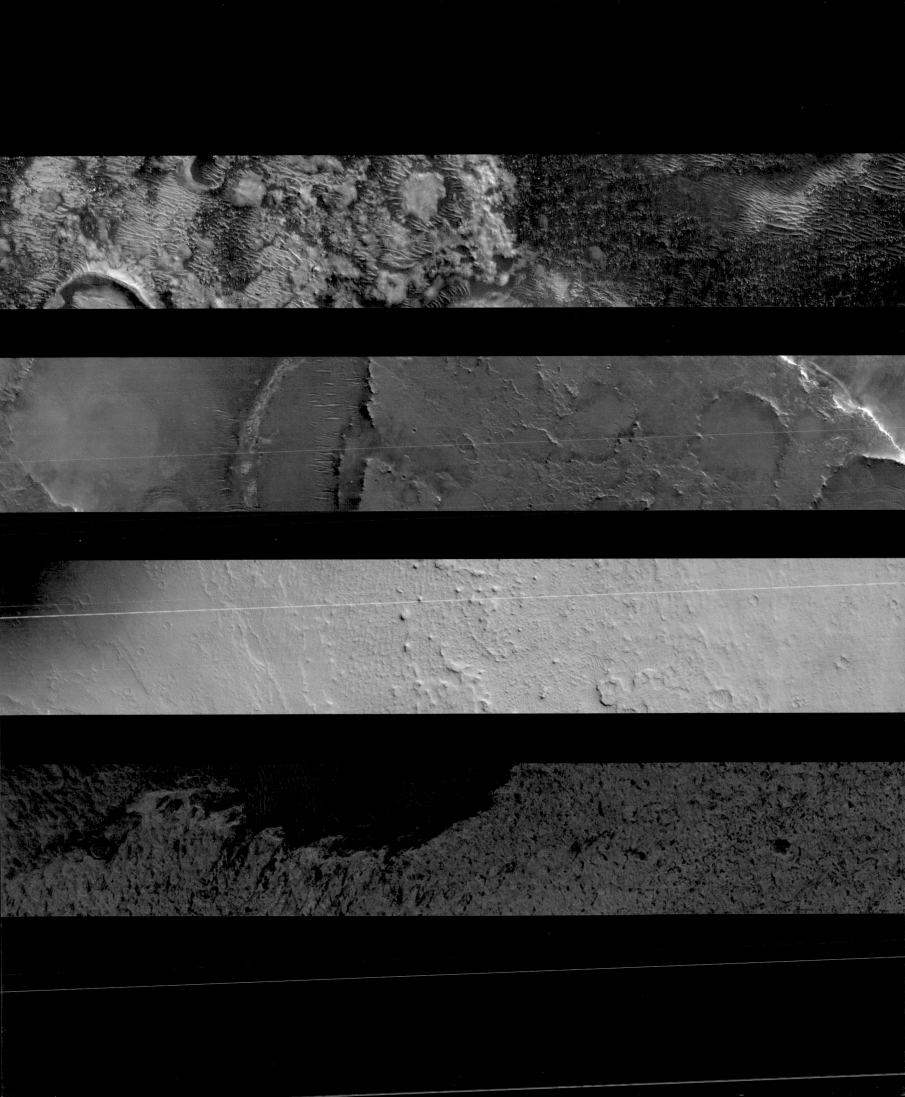

FIRES IN
THE DARKNESS

Fiery tendrils flicker against the opaque dust streams of a star-forming nebula in this montage of radio and visible-light images. Messier 78 is part of the enormous Orion Molecular Complex, a huge region of gas and dust several hundred light years across and around 1,600 light years from Earth, overspilling the bounds of Orion, the Hunter, into neighbouring constellations. Much of the cloud is so faint as to be almost invisible, but in places it erupts into life, bursting with light and activity as it collapses to produce new generations of stars.

Messier 78 is among the brightest of these regions – a series of glowing clouds of light to the northeast of Orion's Belt and just north of the Flame Nebula (see page 26). Detailed views expose it as a distinct pair of clouds criss-crossed by light-absorbing canyons of dust and energized by the radiation from hot blue-white stars within. The region is particularly rich in 'T Tauri' objects – unstable stars that are still fluctuating in size and brightness as they pass through stellar adolescence. Orange streams of light across the nebula's darker regions, meanwhile, mark the infrared emissions from cool grains of dust within the nebula, as detected with the European Southern Observatory's APEX radio telescope.

OBJECT **Messier 78, NGC 2068**

DISTANCE **1,600 light years**

RA **05h 46m 42s**

DEC **+0° 03′ 02″**

OBSERVED WITH **European Southern Observatory**

Atacama Pathfinder Experiment

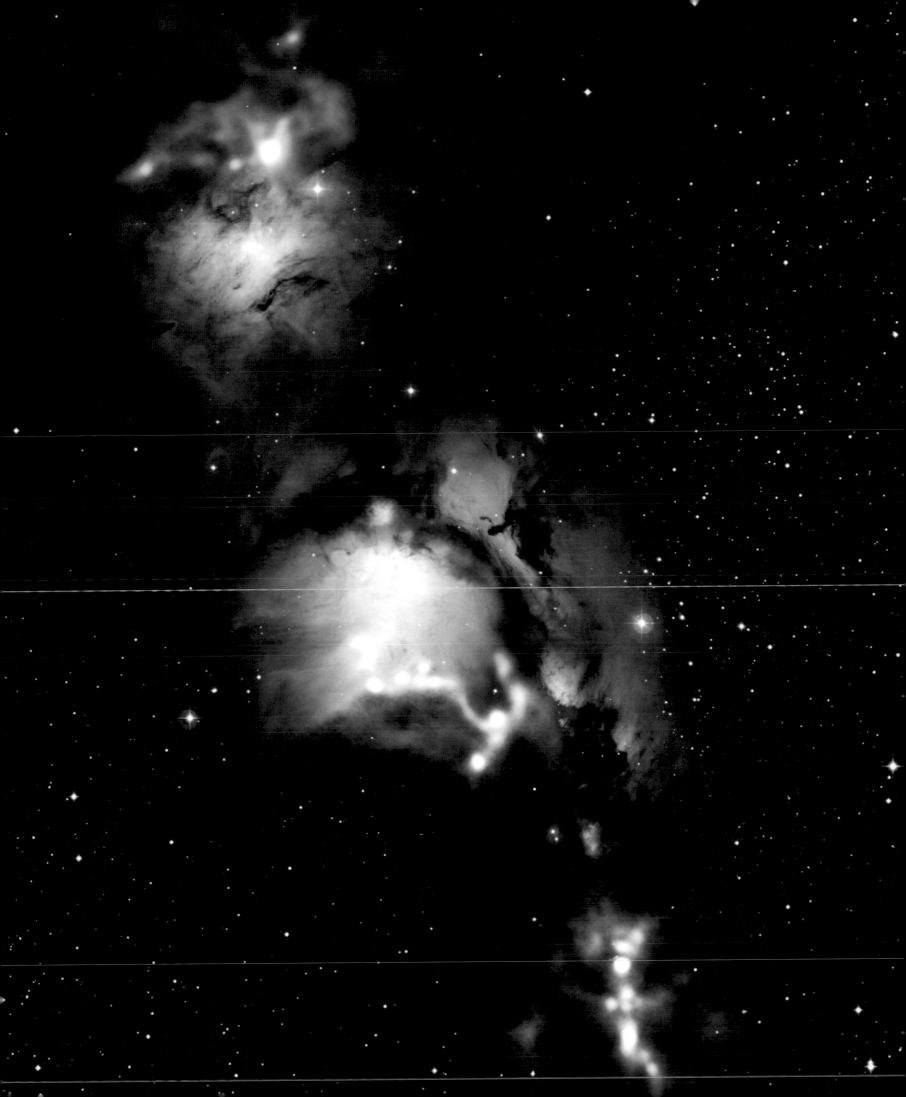

GALACTIC SHADOWPLAY

A trick of perspective results in an image of stunning beauty as one spiral galaxy crosses directly in front of another in the constellation of Hydra. Galaxy NGC 3314 had long been recognized as peculiar in its appearance, but it was only in 1999, when astronomers from the University of Alabama trained the Hubble Space Telescope's powerful gaze towards it, that the truth was revealed. In 2012, Hubble revisited the galaxy pair to create a detailed mosaic using its Advanced Camera for Surveys, resulting in the image shown here.

NGC 3314 is now classified as two separate galaxies. The face-on spiral NGC 3314a lies about 117 million light years from Earth, while the larger NGC 3314b is about 23 million light years further away. As a result, the foreground galaxy's dusty skeleton is silhouetted, while the dusty regions in its more distant partner are lightened by an overlaying 'fog' of intervening stars.

Intriguingly, although the two galaxies are far too distant to be influencing one another, the foreground NGC 3314a shows clear signs of distortion, particularly below and to the right of the central region where a spray of blue stars appears to have unwound from the spiral. This is almost certainly due to a recent encounter with another galaxy that is genuinely in the same region of space.

OBJECT **NGC 3314**

DISTANCE **117–140 million light years**

RA **10h 37m 13s**

DEC **–27° 41' 05"**

OBSERVED WITH **Hubble Space Telescope**

Advanced Camera for Surveys

ABOVE THE CLOUDS

Jupiter's volcanic moon Io hangs placidly above a turbulent cloudscape in this stunning image, which takes full advantage of the forced perspective presented as the Saturn-bound Cassini spaceprobe flew past the giant planet at a distance of 10 million kilometres (6.2 million miles) in December 2000. Jupiter owes its pastel colours to a variety of sulphur-rich chemicals dredged up from deep within the planet's soupy atmosphere. Different chemicals condense from vapour into clouds at different levels in the atmosphere, so that blue clouds mark the deepest layers, brown the intermediate ones and white the uppermost (though the deep red clouds of major storms rise even higher in the atmosphere). Jupiter's rapid rotation creates tremendous coriolis forces that pull the clouds into bands parallel to the planet's bloated equator – light-coloured zones and dark-tinted belts. Rippling streamers of cloud known as festoons reveal the presence of high winds along the edges of the boundaries between them.

Io, meanwhile, is the innermost of the Galilean moons – four worlds, each the size of a small planet, that dominate Jupiter's system of 66 satellites. The browns, reds and yellows of its surface hint at a shared origin to the clouds beneath – Io, like its parent planet, is rich in sulphurous chemicals. Trapped in orbit some 350,000 kilometres (217,000 miles) above Jupiter's cloudtops, Io is subject to powerful tides that tear at its surface and keep its interior molten, providing the energy that makes it the most volcanic body in the solar system.

OBJECT **Io**

SATELLITE OF **Jupiter**

MIN DISTANCE **629 million km (391 million miles)**

DIAMETER **3,643 km (2,264 miles)**

OBSERVED WITH **Cassini Imaging Science Subsystem**

STELLAR GLITTERBALL

Sparkling with the light of tens of thousands of stars, packed into a space just a few light years in diameter, the star cluster Messier 70 forms a brilliant spectacle in this Hubble Space Telescope image. M70 lies about 30,000 light years from Earth, orbiting close to the centre of the Milky Way in the constellation of Sagittarius.

While the majority of our galaxy's star clusters are 'open' clusters, ranging from a few dozen to a few hundred stellar newborns and dominated by short-lived but brilliant massive stars, globular clusters such as M70 contain tens of thousands of rather more average stars in a ball about 68 light years wide. What's more, most have survived intact for about 10 billion years – as long as the Milky Way Galaxy itself. Globular clusters are believed to start out as enormous versions of open clusters, generated during 'starburst' events associated with major galaxy collisions and mergers. While their more massive stars rapidly age and die, the cluster still has enough gravity to hold itself together in a roughly spherical shape (random motions in the more loosely bound open clusters soon see their surviving stars drift apart).

About 20 per cent of globular clusters, including M70, have undergone a further stage of 'core collapse' at some point in their history. This event concentrates most of their stars in an even tighter ball perhaps a dozen light years across, separated by distances of mere light days or even light hours.

OBJECT **Messier 70, NGC 6681**

DISTANCE **29,300 light years**

RA **18h 43m 13s**

DEC **-32° 17' 32"**

OBSERVED WITH **Hubble Space Telescope**
Advanced Camera for Surveys

SATURN AT EQUINOX

Low sunlight creates a gentle glow across Saturn's major rings in an image taken by the Cassini spaceprobe shortly before Saturn's August 2009 equinox. The ringed planet is tilted on its axis at an angle of 27 degrees – just a little more than Earth's own axial tilt – but it takes almost 29.5 years to orbit the Sun and so its seasons each last for more than seven years.

Twice in each long Saturnian year, the planet experiences its equinox, where the Sun lies directly above its equator and day and night are equal in both hemispheres. Since the rings themselves lie directly over Saturn's equator, they experience a perpetual twilight, with the Sun at a very low angle to the ring plane, for several months on either side of the equinox itself. The rings shine only through reflected sunlight, so they are at their faintest at this time, and nearby moons and slight vertical disturbances in the rings cast long shadows across them. In this image, taken from high above Saturn's northern hemisphere, the brightness of the rings has been increased by a factor of almost ten in order to enhance their visibility. In the lower right quadrant of the picture, the rings cast their own razor-sharp shadow across the boundary between Saturnian day and night, while below this, the thin, semi-transparent D ring sweeps almost imperceptibly above the planet's sepia disc.

OBJECT **Saturn**

MIN DISTANCE **1.2 billion km (750 million miles)**

DIAMETER **120,536 km (74,898 miles)**

OBSERVED WITH **Cassini Imaging Science Subsystem**

STEPHAN'S QUINTET

The brightest members of this famous galaxy cluster, discovered in 1877 by French astronomer Edouard Stephan, form impressionistic daubs on the canvas of deep space in this Hubble Space Telescope image. Although these galaxies form a particularly compact group, some 300 million light years from Earth, they also reveal that the darkness between the stars is not as empty as we might think. On their own enormous terms, galaxies are surprisingly crowded together, typically separated from their neighbours by a few times their own diameter at most. The faint light of even more distant galaxies spatter the field beyond the Quintet galaxies themselves.

These startling spirals reveal surprising variety in both colour and structure that hint at the forces unleashed in galactic close encounters. At upper right, an S-shaped spiral displays a long central bar crossed by streams of dark dust, while at lower centre, two bright nuclei reveal the true nature of an object that actually consists of two merging spirals, flinging off chains of stars into nearby space as their spiral arms unwind. Ultimately, these two galaxies will merge together, and perhaps join with their yellowish neighbour. The bluish spiral at upper left, meanwhile, seems unperturbed by these encounters – as well it might, since it is not, in fact, physically linked to the group, but instead lies in the foreground at a distance of a mere 40 million light years.

OBJECT **Stephan's Quintet, HCG 92**

DISTANCE **300 million light years**

RA **22h 35m 58s**

DEC **+33° 57' 36"**

OBSERVED WITH **Hubble Space Telescope**

Wide Field Camera 3

THE MILKY WAY
FROM EARTH

The star-strewn band of the Milky Way wraps its way around the heavens in this pin-sharp panorama of the sky, a mosaic gathered by European Southern Observatory astronomers over several months. The image encompasses the entire northern and southern hemispheres of Earth's sky – the inner surface of the illusory 'celestial sphere' that appears to wrap around Earth, spinning once a day on an axis fixed above the north and south poles. The sphere's rotation is of course deceptive – in truth, the result of Earth's rotation within the more or less fixed panoply of the heavens. Only the Sun, Moon and other solar system objects move against this backdrop at appreciable speed, although the reality is that every shining star, glowing nebula and distant galaxy is in motion.

Under truly dark skies, typical human eyesight can pick out only 3,000 stars at any one time – roughly 6,000 across the entire sky. Their light may have taken years, centuries, millennia or even longer to make the long journey to Earth. Light from the Magellanic Clouds – small satellite galaxies of our own, visible below the Milky Way in this image – takes 180,000 to 210,000 years to reach us. That from the Andromeda Galaxy, our nearest large neighbour in space, takes around 2.5 million years. The Andromeda system marks the limit of our vision, but the enormous unblinking eyes of giant telescopes can sweep up the faint light of far more distant galaxies, millions or even billions of light years away.

OBJECT **The Milky Way Galaxy**

DISTANCE **26,000 light years (to centre)**

RA **N/A**

DEC **N/A**

OBSERVED WITH **European Southern Observatory**

GigaGalaxy Zoom Project

ANTENNAE GALAXIES

Clouds of red and blue mark sources of invisible radiation overlying a stunning Hubble Space Telescope image of galaxies in the turmoil of a cosmic collision. The Antennae Galaxies, NGC 4038 and NGC 4039, are a pair of merging galaxies in the obscure constellation of Corvus, around 45 million light years from Earth. They get their name from distorted spiral arms that stretch away on either side of their bright centre.

The heart of this interacting system, meanwhile, offers an unusual detailed view of a galactic merger. During any encounter of this type, head-on collisions between individual stars are rare. The real action is driven by interstellar gas clouds slamming into each other and unleashing enormous waves of star formation. Hubble pictures in visible light alone show how these starbursts are illuminating the structure of the merging galaxies, but this composite adds an infrared image (red) showing where newborn stars are heating interstellar dust – and an X-ray image (blue) revealing a halo of gas heated to extreme temperatures by the collision.

OBJECT **Antennae Galaxies, NGC 4038/9**

DISTANCE **45 million light years**

RA **12h 01m 54s**

DEC **-18° 52' 36"**

OBSERVED WITH

Hubble Space Telescope,

Chandra X-Ray Observatory,

Spitzer Space Telescope

➤ OPPOSITE

AN EXPLODING GALAXY

At first glance, it seems as if the red streaks in this beautiful Hubble Space Telescope image might be entirely disconnected from the rest of the scene, simply daubed onto the canvas of an otherwise placid galaxy. But then one notices the way in which the streaks appear to radiate from the galaxy's centre, and the fact that this long ellipse of stars – fittingly nicknamed the Cigar Galaxy – is remarkably bright for its size. Small wonder that it was once described as an 'exploding galaxy'.

M82 lies some 11.5 million light years from Earth in the constellation of Ursa Major. It is now viewed as the prototype 'starburst' galaxy – a system in which star formation is proceeding at a tremendous rate (ten times faster than in the Milky Way) due to the influence of the nearby spiral galaxy M81. This accelerated starbirth also boosts the rate of star death among massive, short-lived stars and, as the exploding supernovae heat up the gases around them, they accelerate it to such speeds that the gas escapes the galaxy's weak gravity entirely, giving Messier 82 its extraordinary appearance.

OBJECT **Cigar Galaxy, M82**

DISTANCE **11.5 million light years**

RA **09h 55m 52s**

DEC **+69° 49' 47"**

OBSERVED WITH

Hubble Space Telescope

Advanced Camera for Surveys

➤➤ OVERLEAF

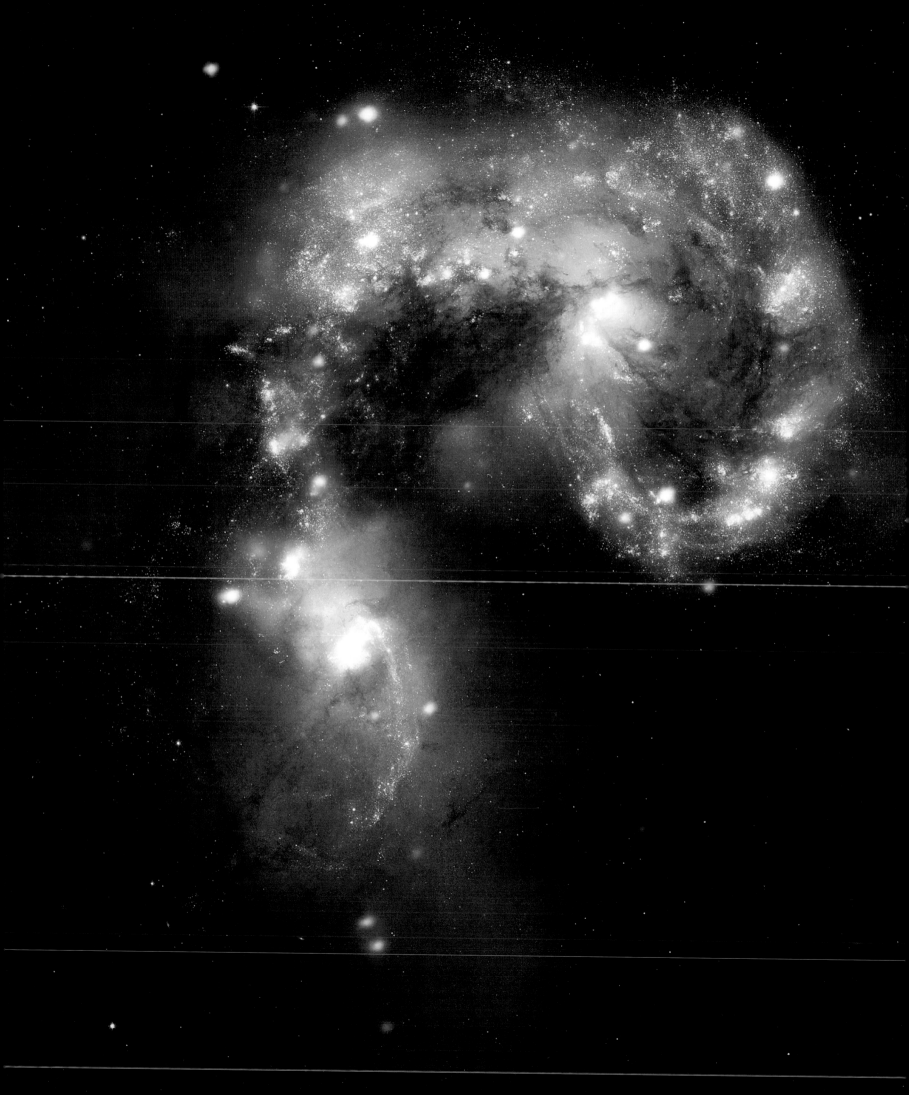

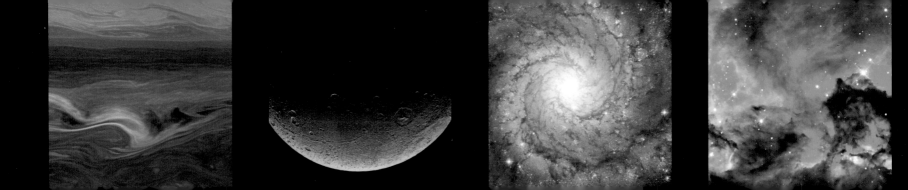

ORDER AND CHAOS 2

CRATERED MERCURY

Rainbow colours render the surface of Mercury into a pop-art landscape in this radar map of Goethe Basin in the planet's northern hemisphere. Altitudes across this lowland plain, roughly 320 kilometres (200 miles) across, vary by about 1 kilometre (0.6 miles) between the deepest purples and blues, and the highest reds and greys.

Constructed using the radar altimetry instrument aboard NASA's MESSENGER spaceprobe, the colours of this radar map help highlight subtle features within the basin. Concentric ringed ranges of hills mark the ghostly outlines of the initial crater, produced by a massive impact on the planet's ancient surface. Cracked areas suggest regions in which the surface has subsided further after the crater's formation, while 'wrinkles' can also be traced across the baking Mercurial terrain.

Lying at a high northern latitude, some of the deep craters within Goethe are never fully illuminated by Mercury's fierce daylight – instead, with no atmosphere to aid the circulation of heat, these crater floors languish forever at temperatures of around -190°C (-310°F). Intriguingly, these crater floors are unusually 'radar-bright', reflecting strong signals that suggest they may be filled with smooth, reflective material, such as ice. If such ice is really present, then it has probably accumulated in Mercury's colder regions thanks to billions of years of impacts from ice-laden comets.

OBJECT **Mercury**

MIN DISTANCE **77.3 million km (48 million miles)**

DIAMETER **4,879 km (3,032 miles)**

OBSERVED WITH **MESSENGER Mercury Laser Altimeter**

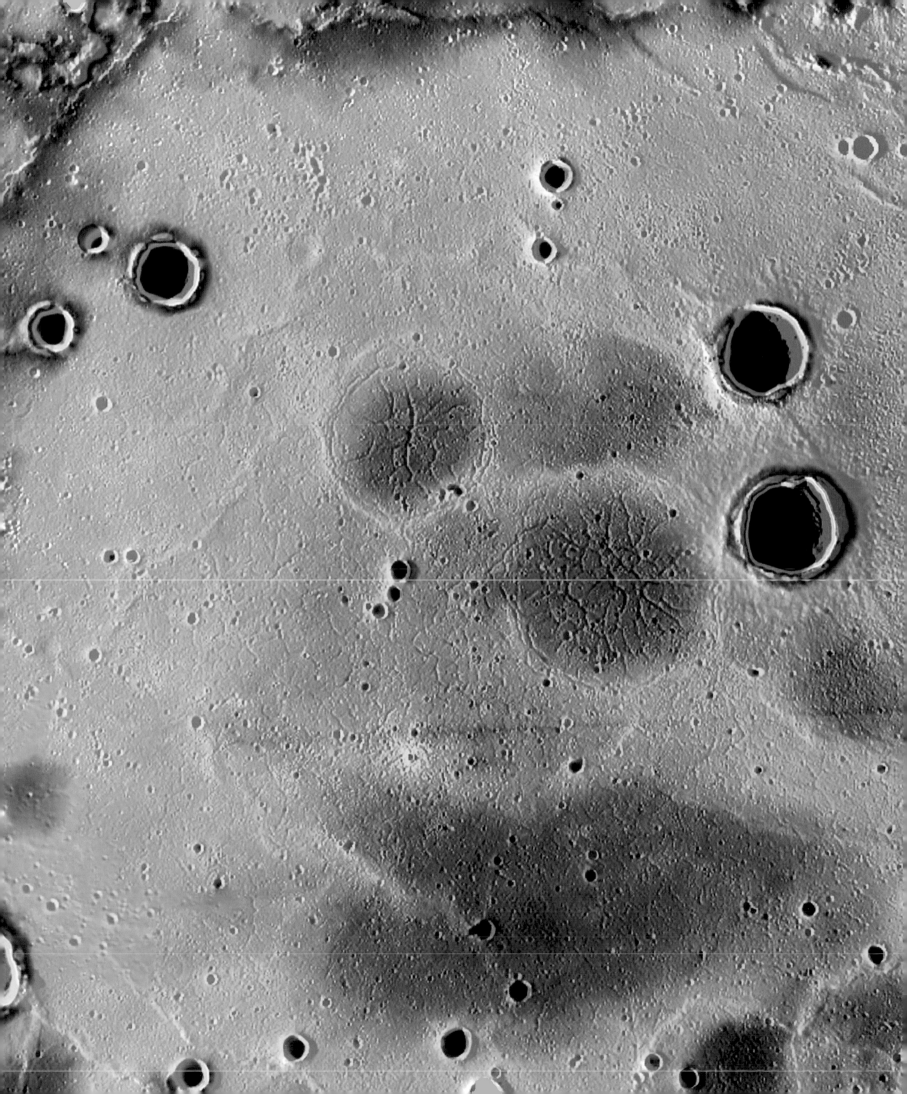

VENUS LAID BARE

This stark, false-coloured radar map strips away the mystery of our nearest planetary neighbour to reveal the geological reality of a world shaped almost exclusively by volcanic activity. Colours ranging from dark blue, through greens and yellows to pink and white, represent the range of elevations from lowland plains to highland plateaus across a world that is Earth's near-twin in terms of size, but a startling contrast in almost every other respect.

Venus is our morning and evening 'star', the brightest object in the sky aside from the Sun and Moon, and fittingly named after the Roman goddess of beauty. A veil of brilliant clouds forever hides her surface, transforming our inner neighbour in the solar system into a dazzling orb of mysterious light.

Before the Space Age, astronomers and writers freely speculated that this seemingly placid beauty might conceal a humid, hospitable world, perhaps strewn with forests and inhabited by intelligent life. However, modern technology has revealed a more sobering truth – early spaceprobes plunging into the atmosphere failed when confronted with an unexpectedly hellish environment, simultaneously crushed by tremendous atmospheric pressure, burnt by acidic vapours and melted by furnace temperatures that rarely fall below 460°C (830°F). As a result, it is only with the aid of radar mapping – first using Earth-based radio telescopes, and later from orbiting spaceprobes – that scientists have been able to map the planet's geography in detail.

OBJECT **Venus**

MIN DISTANCE **38.2 million km (23.7 million miles)**

DIAMETER **12,104 km (7,521 miles)**

OBSERVED WITH **Magellan RDRS Radar System**

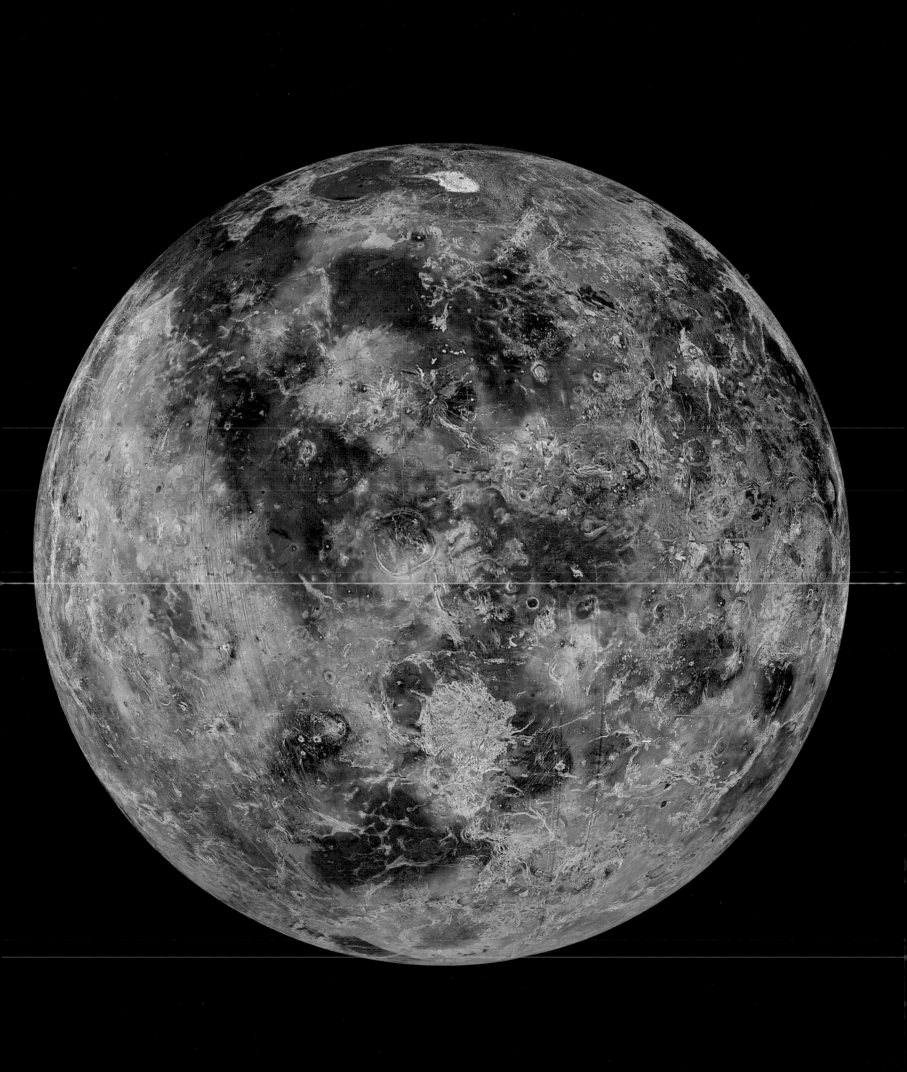

CELESTIAL SURF

In a composition reminiscent of a furious sea, boiling clouds of gas pile up at the edges of Messier 17, a star-forming nebula some 5,500 light years away in the constellation of Sagittarius. In this Hubble Space Telescope image, covering an area roughly three light years across, pastel colours represent various energized gases within the nebula: red indicates the presence of sulphur, green reveals hydrogen and blue shows oxygen.

Commonly known as the Omega Nebula – from its supposed resemblance to the Greek capital Ω – or the Swan Nebula, Messier 17 is roughly 15 light years in diameter and contains an estimated 800 solar masses of material. It was discovered by Swiss astronomer Jean-Philippe Loys de Chéseaux in 1745, and lies in the midst of dense star clouds towards the centre of our Milky Way Galaxy.

This turbulent cloudscape is sculpted by light from a cluster of brilliant young stars near the centre of the nebula (outside of the picture at upper left). As their ultraviolet radiation cuts away at the surrounding clouds of cold molecular hydrogen, it carves the intricate three-dimensional patterns seen here, with the heated surfaces glowing orange and red. Lightweight hydrogen atoms are heated enough to stream away from the denser clouds, creating the greenish glow across the centre of the nebula.

OBJECT **Omega Nebula, M17**

DISTANCE **5,500 light years**

RA **18h 20m 46s**

DEC **-16° 09' 27"**

OBSERVED WITH **Hubble Space Telescope**

Wide Field and Planetary Camera 2

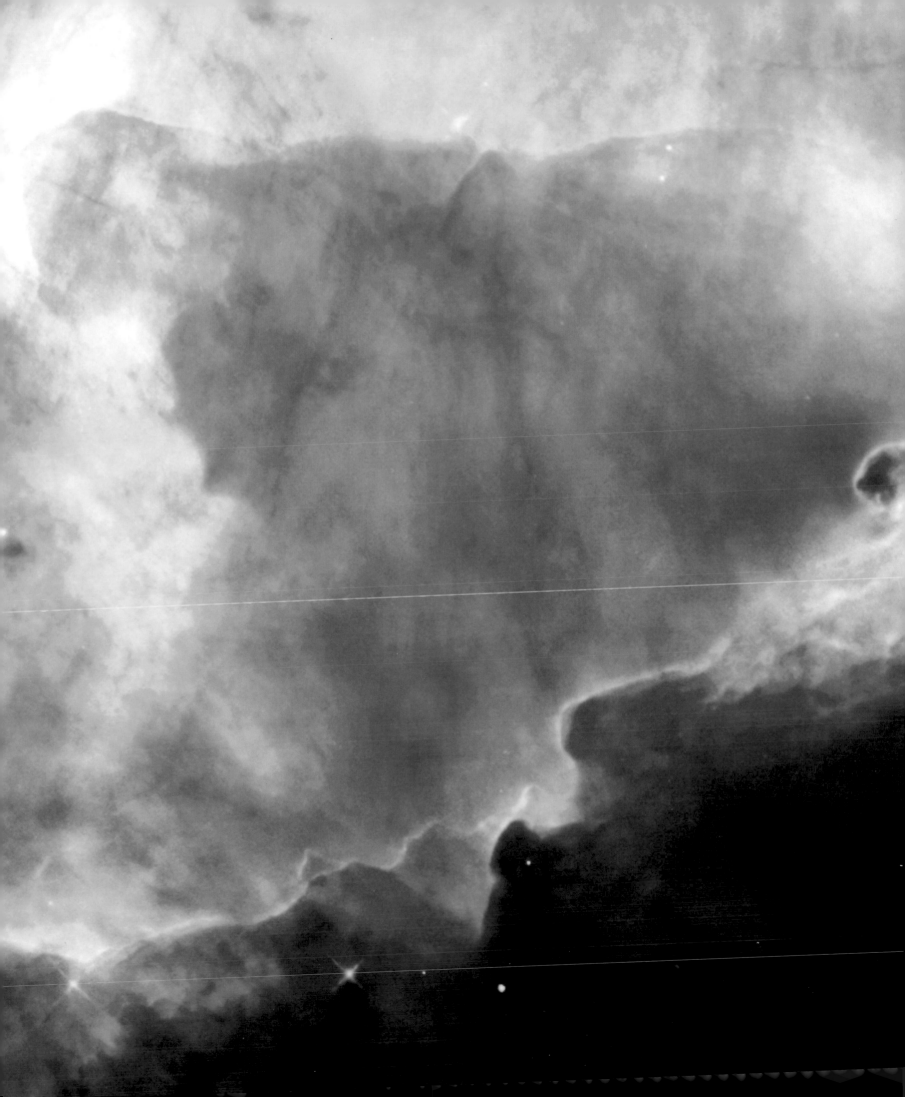

TITAN'S MYSTERIOUS ATMOSPHERE

A perfect alignment snapped by the Cassini spaceprobe showcases the intricate dynamics of Saturn's satellite and ring system. Everything in this seemingly placid image is in fact in motion – the giant moon Titan in the foreground, the smaller satellite Dione beyond it and the rings and cream-clouded planet in the background. The plane of the rings themselves creates a stark line across the middle of the composition, while the lower half is filled with a multitude of dark stripes created by ring shadows cast across Saturn's sepia globe.

The clouds of Saturn provide an unusual backdrop to Titan, revealing the hazy tan layers of the moon's outer atmosphere. Titan has the thickest atmosphere of any satellite in the solar system – one that bears some startling similarities to Earth's own primordial air. While it is dominated by nitrogen, it contains a small but significant percentage of hydrocarbon chemicals, predominantly methane. Sunlight penetrating through the haze should rapidly destroy atmospheric methane, so either it was much more plentiful in the past, or it must be continuously regenerated by chemical processes, such as 'cryovolcanism' – an icy, low-temperature equivalent to the volcanism found in rocky worlds such as Earth. According to the latest estimates, this 'methane factory' has probably been running for around a billion years.

OBJECT **Titan**

SATELLITE OF **Saturn**

MIN DISTANCE **1.2 billion km (750 million miles)**

DIAMETER **5,152 km (3,201 miles)**

OBSERVED WITH **Cassini Imaging Science Subsystem**

FROSTS OF MARS

Surprising patterns emerge from the desert sands at the onset of spring in this image from NASA's Mars Reconnaissance Orbiter. The northern hemisphere of Mars is dominated by a vast lowland plain known as the Vastitas Borealis, thought to have formed after a vast impact that liquefied part of the planet's surface shortly after its formation. Today, the plain is dominated by a huge dune sea in which countless mounds of fine sand, sculpted by the prevailing winds, pile up on top of denser underlying soils.

Mars has a pattern of seasons very like Earth's, although temperatures are much lower. At the onset of each northern winter, carbon dioxide ice condenses from the atmosphere to form a thin layer of frost that caps both sand and soil, freezing it in place. As spring returns and the climate warms, the frosts begin to sublimate, returning directly to the atmosphere as gas. Bluish cracks show where this process is underway, while the dark patches around the base of some dunes show where the protective frost has completely disappeared, allowing winds to blow the sand away.

OBJECT **Mars**

MIN DISTANCE **54.6 million km (33.9 million miles)**

DIAMETER **6,792 km (4,220 miles)**

OBSERVED WITH

Mars Reconnaissance Orbiter High-Resolution Imaging Science Experiment

➤ OPPOSITE

SATURNIAN SUPERSTORM

Resembling the turbulent patterns formed by inks floating on water, this pair of vividly false-coloured images chronicle the development of a swirling storm wrapped around Saturn's northern hemisphere. The two mosaic pictures, each containing 84 separate images taken over 4.5 hours, were taken by NASA's Cassini spaceprobe, in orbit around the ringed planet, about 11 hours (one Saturnian day) apart in February 2011.

In normal light, Saturn's clouds are far less colourful than Jupiter's – dominated by a creamy layer of ammonia at high altitudes that give the planet a sepia tint. Major bright storms known as white spots typically erupt at 30-year intervals, the most recent of which were in the early 1990s, so the sudden outburst of an intense white storm in late 2010 came as a surprise to astronomers. It rapidly spread around the planet, emitting blasts of electromagnetic energy as it grew to 300,000 kilometres (186,000 miles) long and 15,000 kilometres (9,000 miles) wide. In this false-colour mosaic taken at near-infrared wavelengths, cool areas are shown in blue and warmer ones in red.

OBJECT **Saturn**

MIN DISTANCE **1.2 billion km (750 million miles)**

DIAMETER **120,536 km (74,898 miles)**

OBSERVED WITH **Cassini Imaging Science Subsystem**

➤ ➤ OVERLEAF

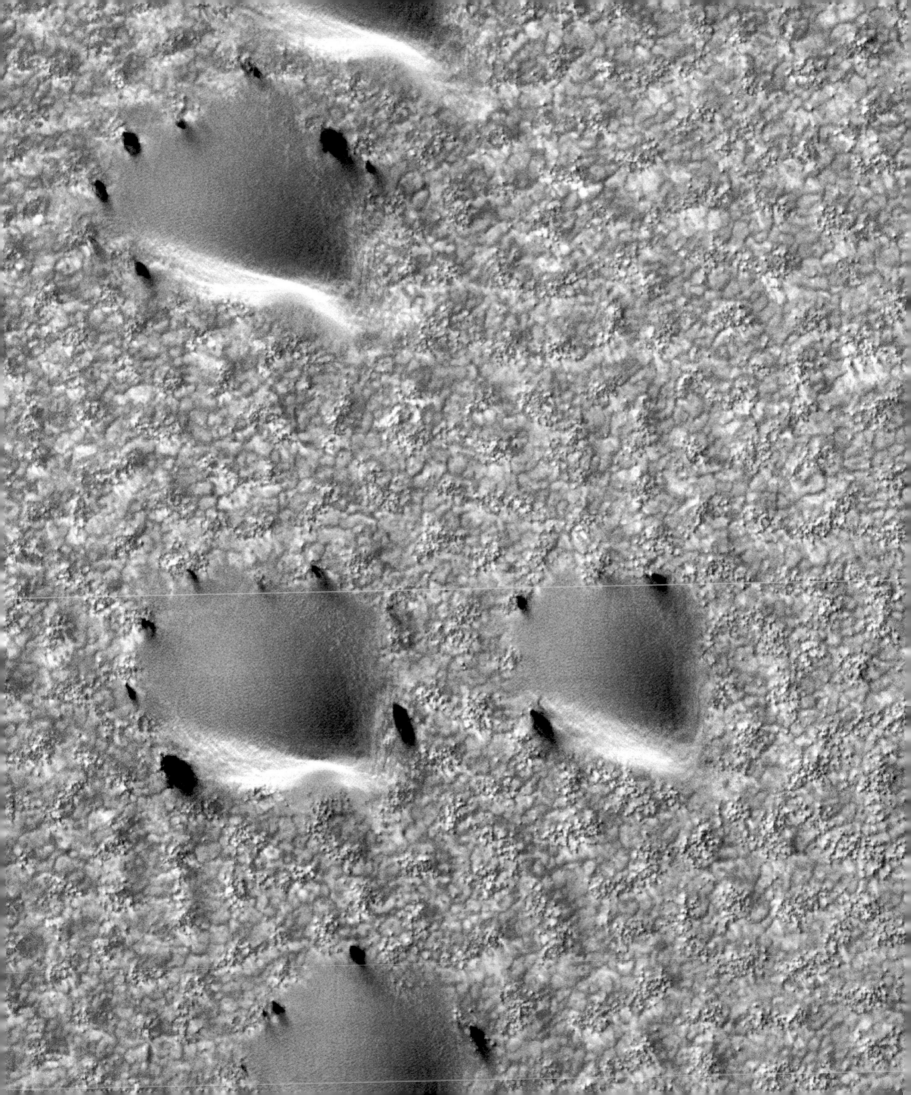

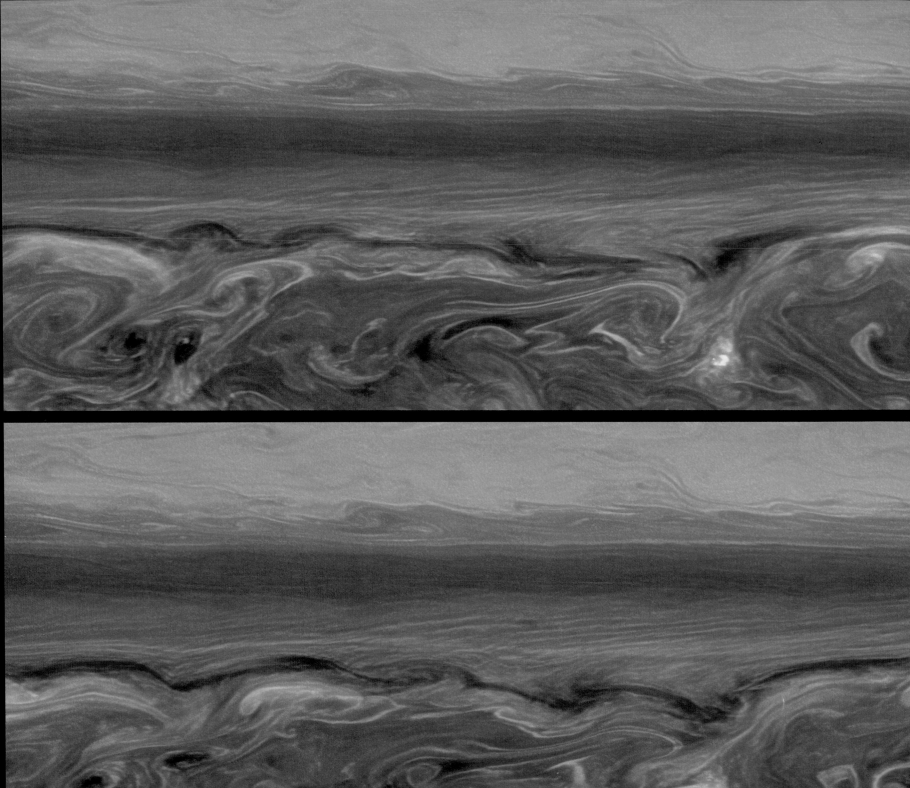

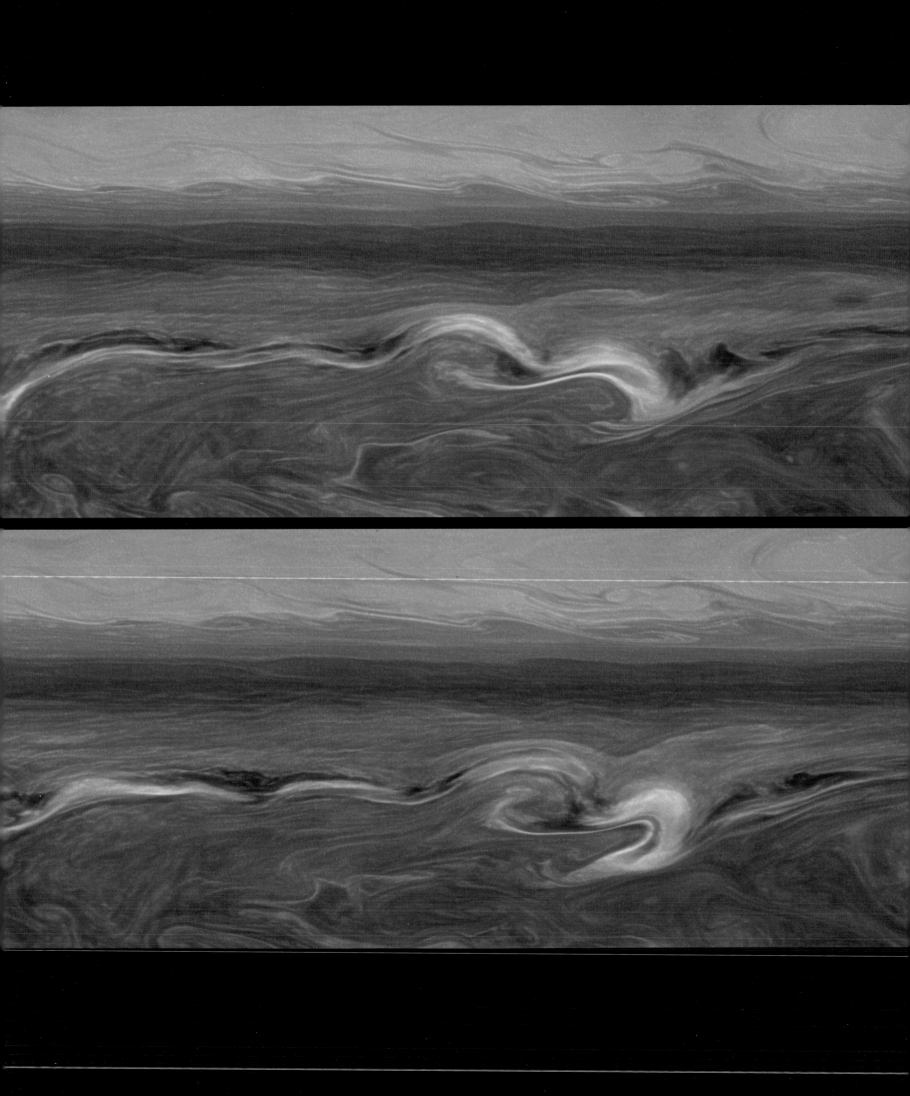

VENUSIAN VOLCANO

Looking like a splatter of paint thrown against a planetary canvas, the shallow flanks of a twin-peaked volcano dominate this false-coloured radar map of the Venusian surface. Thanks to a 'synthetic aperture' radar technique more commonly used by Earth-orbiting satellites, NASA's Magellan spaceprobe was able to peel away the dense, toxic atmosphere of Venus to map the planet's surface in unprecedented detail. The mission, which lasted from 1989 to 1993, mapped not only topography (surface elevation), but also properties such as roughness and reflectivity that, when combined with colours 'borrowed' from the photographs of Venusian landers, create images such as this.

The Sapas Mons volcano at the centre of this image is roughly 400 kilometres (250 miles) across, but rises to a maximum elevation of only 1.5 kilometres (0.9 miles). Lava flows along its flanks resemble those found in large Earth volcanoes such as the Hawaiian islands. Sapas Mons is thought to have formed when an underground magma reservoir erupted through numerous fissures along its flanks. A series of pits near its peak show how the surface collapsed back on itself as the magma drained away, while two mesas (raised plateaus) mark its current peak. A nearby crater, partly buried by lava, is a rare survivor – the face of Venus is remarkably craterless, having been largely resurfaced by a burst of volcanic activity that is thought to have begun around 600 million years ago and may still rumble on today.

OBJECT **Venus**

MIN DISTANCE **38.2 million km (23.7 million miles)**

DIAMETER **12,104 km (7,521 miles)**

OBSERVED WITH **Magellan RDRS Radar System**

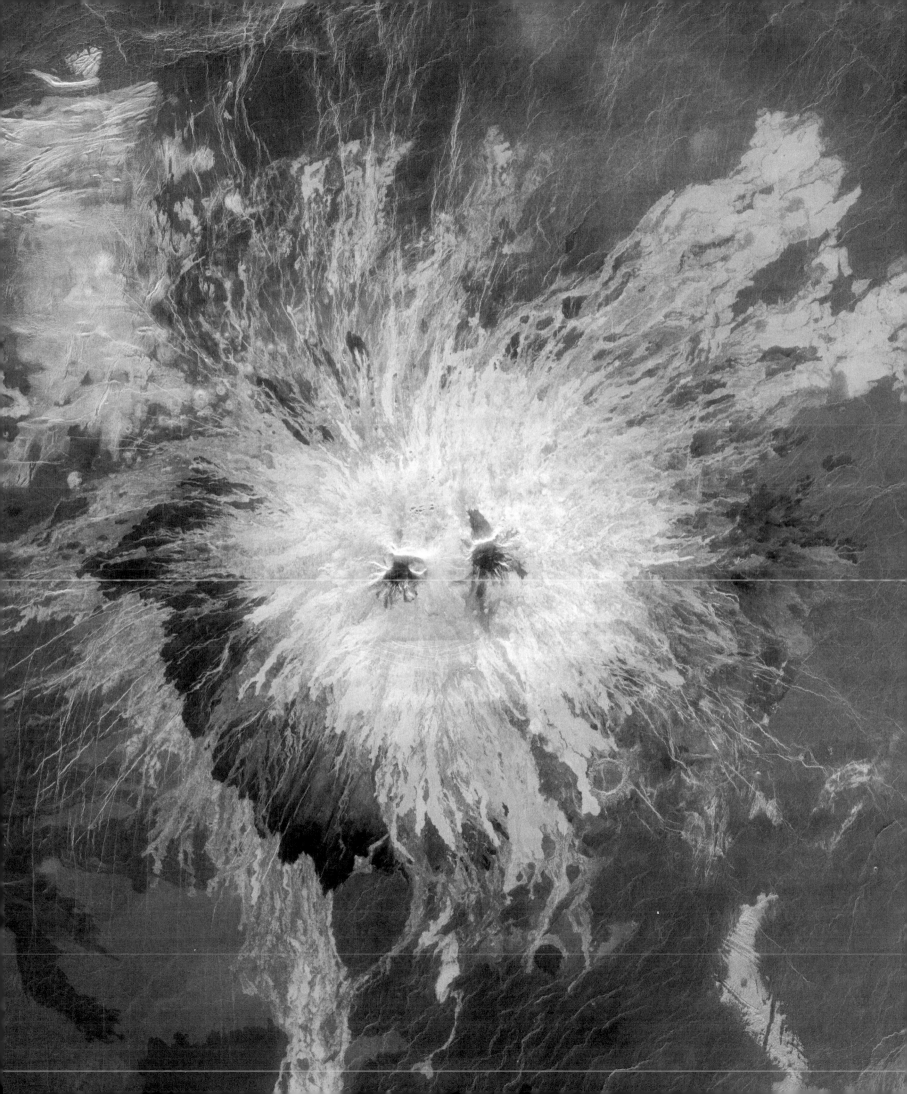

FIRESTORM OF
STARBIRTH

At first glance this abstract scene, dominated by tattered, glowing clouds above an ominously dark and misshapen landscape, gives only the vaguest hint of its true meaning. But here and there, a few stars shine through the haze – these are among the youngest newly formed residents of the Carina Nebula, one of the most celebrated regions of star formation in our galaxy, some 7,500 light years from Earth.

This Hubble Space Telescope view captures only a small region within the huge nebula, perhaps 20 light years across. As with all such objects, the nebula is in a state of constant flux – star formation here is thought to have begun around 3 million years ago, since when several generations of infant stars have emerged from their birth cocoons and begun to shine. Fierce radiation from the brightest of these stars has made short work of hollowing out the nebula from within, and dark clouds along the bottom of the image mark out one part of the 'shock front' where gas is currently being beaten back.

Trunk-like protuberances emerge from the haze directly above this cloudfront, marking denser regions in which the next generation of stars is forming. Held together by stronger gravity, they cast protective shadows that connect them ever more tenuously to the bulk of dark clouds. However permanent they appear, these 'pillars of creation' are mere temporary structures – in places they have already lost much of their volume, disintegrating to become isolated star-forming clumps known as Bok globules.

OBJECT **Carina Nebula, NGC 3372**

DISTANCE **7,500 light years**

RA **10h 45m 09s**

DEC **-59° 52' 04"**

OBSERVED WITH **Hubble Space Telescope**

Advanced Camera for Surveys

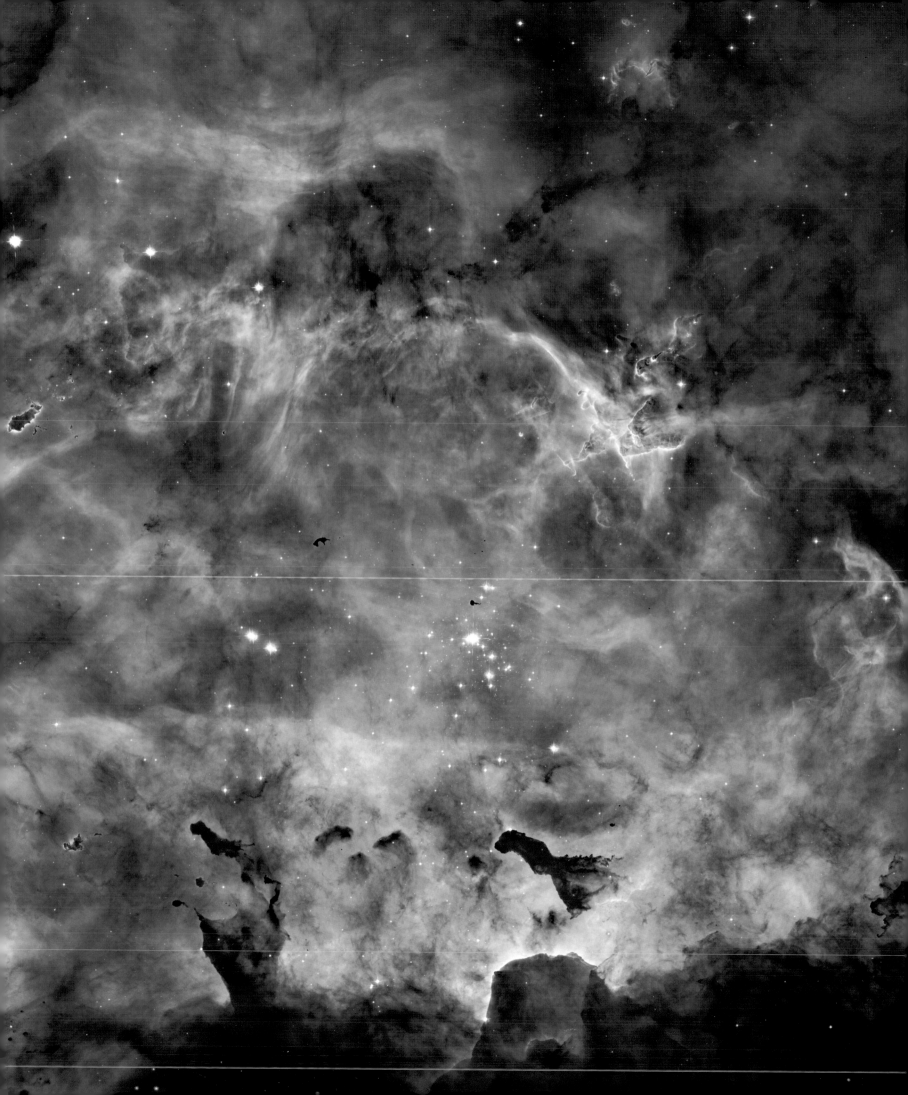

GRAND DESIGN

Unfathomably complicated yet geometrically simple, galaxy Messier 74 offers up its detailed structure of dust lanes, star clusters and nebulae for our inspection. Blue-white knots of light indicate newly formed open clusters dominated by the galaxy's brightest stars, while pinkish blooms show where star formation is presently underway. Meanwhile, a haze of countless indistinguishable background stars – average stars like our own Sun – silhouettes the galaxy's dark, rippled skeleton of inactive gas and light-absorbing dust. At the centre of the image, the density of stars increases towards the unresolvable blaze of light marking the galaxy's hub.

Messier 74 lies around 32 million light years from Earth in the constellation of Pisces, and provides a stunning example of a so-called 'grand design' spiral galaxy. In this model system, the spiral structure is defined by young, brilliant star clusters whose formation is triggered as gas and dust in the galaxy's flattened disc moves through a spiral compression zone or 'density wave'. This wave pattern is a semi-permanent feature, created when the individual elliptical orbits of objects around the galactic hub are all pulled in a certain direction by tidal forces (in this case probably produced by nearby companion galaxies). Other galaxies, including our own, are more complex – when the tidal forces get too great or galaxies actually collide, the pattern can be easily disrupted, while if there are no suitable forces at work, the density wave can dissipate, leaving behind a 'flocculent' spiral in which star formation is concentrated in clumps governed by localized forces.

OBJECT **Messier 74, NGC 628**

DISTANCE **32 million light years**

RA **01h 36m 42s**

DEC **+15° 47' 01"**

OBSERVED WITH **Hubble Space Telescope**

Advanced Camera for Surveys

HOMEWORLD

Low rays of sunlight turn the Southern Ocean between South America and Antarctica golden in this serene view of a crescent Earth, captured by the European Space Agency's Rosetta spaceprobe during its 2009 fly-by. Our planet is unique in the solar system for its abundant surface water, often attributed to its position in the 'Goldilocks zone' of moderate temperatures. But our temperate climate is also due in large part to the substantial size of Earth itself. Our planet is the largest solid body in the solar system, and its substantial gravity allows it to hold onto a protective, insulating atmosphere. What is more, the mix of the planet's rotation and axial tilt produces a pattern of days and seasons that ensure a fairly even distribution of temperatures between poles and tropics.

As a result, more than two-thirds of Earth is covered in deep oceans. The transformation of water between liquid, vapour and ice is a crucial force in shaping our planet's surface and encouraging its abundance of life. It even plays a role in lubricating the tectonic plates that make up the fragmented crust, encouraging the forces of continent building and destruction that keep Earth in a state of constant dynamic change.

Launched in 2004, the Rosetta spaceprobe's convoluted flight path has seen it spend almost a decade touring the inner solar system, flying past Earth, Mars and several asteroids on its way to a final rendezvous with Comet Churyumov-Gerasimenko in 2014.

OBJECT **Earth**

DISTANCE **N/A**

DIAMETER **12,756 km (7,926 miles)**

OBSERVED WITH **Rosetta OSIRIS**
(Optical, Spectroscopic and Infrared
Remote Imaging System)

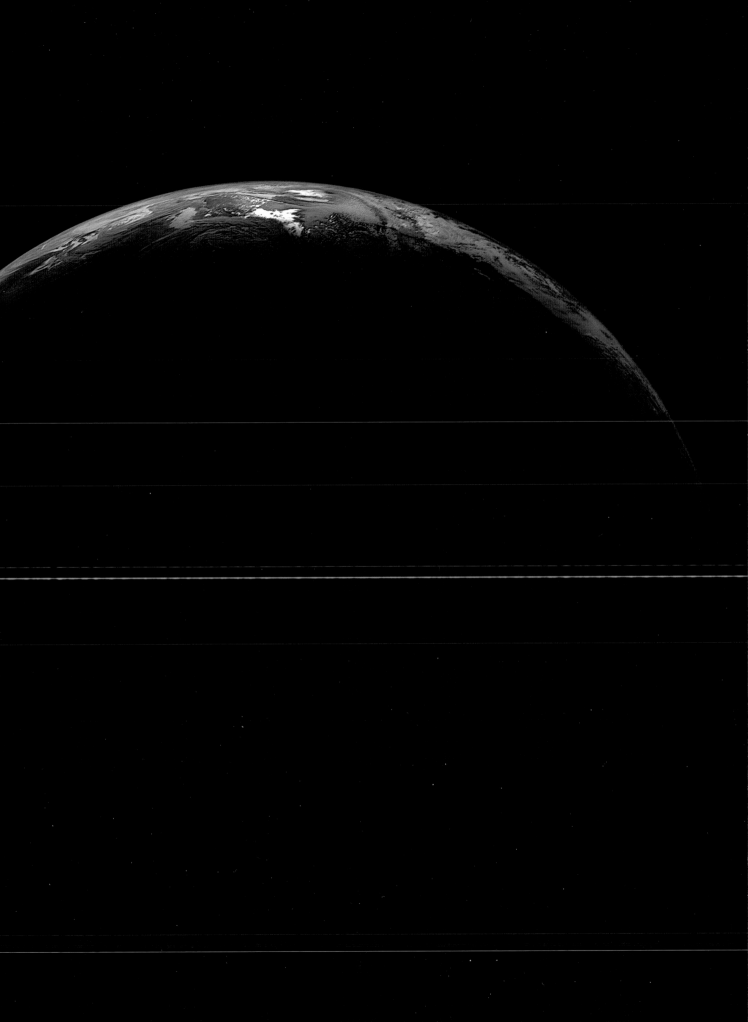

DEVIL TRACKS

Dark swirls across the rippled dunes of a Martian desert form an unexpected display of natural calligraphy in this remarkable image from NASA's Mars Reconnaissance Orbiter. When first discovered, these curious tracks presented a puzzle to planetary scientists, but they are now known to be the handiwork of Martian dust devils.

Just as on Earth, dust devils on Mars are formed by columns of hot air rising through cooler layers of air above. In the right circumstances, the column can begin to rotate and grow in size, developing into a relatively long-lived whirlwind that draws up loose material as it sweeps across the ground. On Earth, dust devils rarely grow to more than a few metres in diameter and are usually fairly harmless, but in the thin Martian atmosphere they can grow much larger and involve much higher windspeeds. Furthermore, because Martian sands are typically much finer than the soils of Earth, dust devils can loft much more of it into the air on Mars, scouring the upper layers of the desert to reveal darker underlying material. The process has now been photographed in action both from the ground and from orbit.

In 2005, a passing dust devil did an unexpected favour to NASA engineers by clearing away dust from the solar panels of the Mars Exploration Rover *Spirit*, boosting its energy supplies. However, mission planners take seriously the possibility that a future encounter with a large dust devil might have more damaging effects on a Martian rover.

OBJECT **Mars**

MIN DISTANCE **54.6 million km (33.9 million miles)**

DIAMETER **6,792 km (4,220 miles)**

OBSERVED WITH **Mars Reconnaissance Orbiter**

High-Resolution Imaging Science Experiment

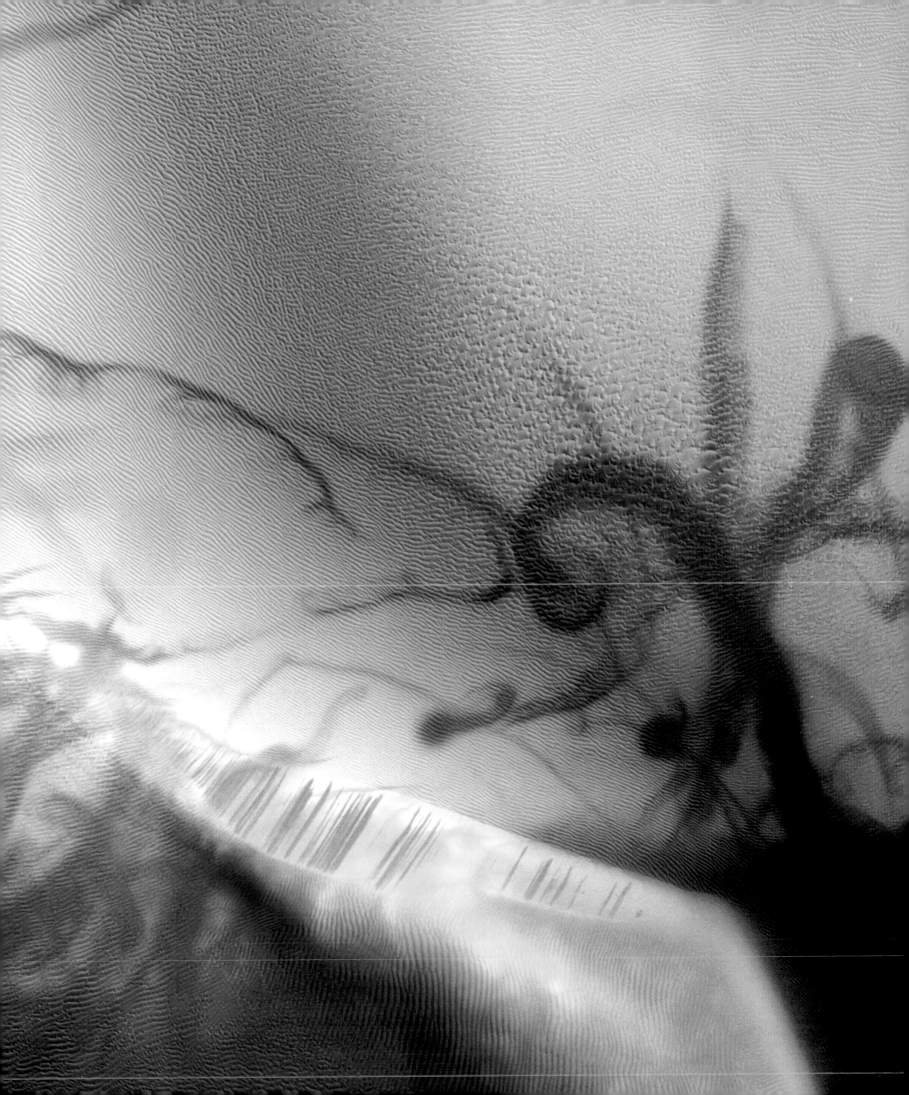

STARBURST

Suspended like a glittering firework in space, star cluster NGC 3603 is framed by the remnants of the nebula that gave it life in this beautiful Hubble Space Telescope image. This open star cluster, roughly 20,000 light years away in the Carina spiral arm of our galaxy, is one of the densest known, and contains some of the brightest stars in the Milky Way. When British astronomer John Herschel discovered it while observing from South Africa in 1834, he first suspected it might be a globular cluster. The surrounding nebulosity is impressive, too – while it pales in comparison to the much closer and brighter Carina Nebula (see page 64), it is in fact the largest star-forming region known in our galaxy – this image spans only the central 17 light years.

At the centre of the cluster, stars are too closely packed to distinguish from one another visually. However, other techniques have confirmed that NGC 3603 has several remarkable star systems at its heart. The NGC 3603-A1 system, for instance, is a double blue star of which the more massive component is the heaviest known star in our galaxy, with the mass of 116 Suns. Its companion is no lightweight either, weighing in at an estimated 89 solar masses. Torrents of radiation from these fearsome stars have cleared out a substantial hollow in the surrounding nebula, but the compression waves they create may also be crucial to triggering new outbreaks of starbirth.

OBJECT **NGC 3603**

DISTANCE **20,000 light years**

RA **11h 15m 09s**

DEC **-61° 16' 17"**

OBSERVED WITH **Hubble Space Telescope**
Advanced Camera for Surveys

SATELLITE MAPPING

A unique map projection imposes geometric order onto the apparently chaotic surface of Ganymede, Jupiter's biggest moon and the largest satellite in the solar system. Map projections are an artificial solution to the perennial problem of representing a spherical surface on a flat page – in this case, the answer is to combine a traditional Mercator projection for low latitudes (the 'petals') with a special equal-area projection for the north polar region, minimizing the distortion of both shapes and areas.

Ganymede is an intriguing world, larger than Mercury. While its mottled grey surface seems unspectacular compared to the volcanic plains of Io and the brilliant icefields of Europa, it has clearly had a complex and active past. Tidal forces acting on it were once much greater than they are today – sufficient to partially melt Ganymede's mixture of rock and ice, allowing parts of the cratered ancient crust to subside, while fresh ice welled up from beneath to fill the gaps. Residual heat from these ancient upheavals may still be enough to maintain a thin saltwater ocean just beneath Ganymede's crust.

OBJECT **Ganymede**

SATELLITE OF **Jupiter**

MIN DISTANCE **629 million km**
(391 million miles)

DIAMETER **5,262 km (3,280 miles)**

OBSERVED WITH **Galileo**
Solid-State Imager

➤ OPPOSITE

GREAT RED SPOT

Jupiter's swirling clouds resemble thickly layered oils applied to the canvas of the planet's atmosphere in this stunning image from the Voyager spaceprobe. Deep canyons, kilometres deep, surround the central plateau of the Great Red Spot, a slowly spinning storm large enough to swallow Earth whole, while cloud lanes to either side are rippled into countless intricate folds.

The spot is Jupiter's most famous feature. Lying a little way to the south of the planet's equator, it is an enormous region of high pressure, slowly rotating anticlockwise and rising to 8 kilometres (5 miles) above the surrounding cloudtops. The storm draws up material from deeper within the atmosphere, and as complex chemicals (perhaps compounds of sulphur or phosphorus) condense at high altitudes, they give rise to its vivid colours. The spot's intensity can vary over time, and on rare occasions it loses its colour altogether, leaving just a 'hollow' to mark its position. Recent observations suggest that the spot sustains itself by feeding on surrounding weather systems.

OBJECT **Jupiter**

MIN DISTANCE **629 million km**
(391 million miles)

DIAMETER **142,984 km (88,846 miles)**

OBSERVED WITH **Voyager 1**
Imaging Science Subsystem

➤➤ OVERLEAF

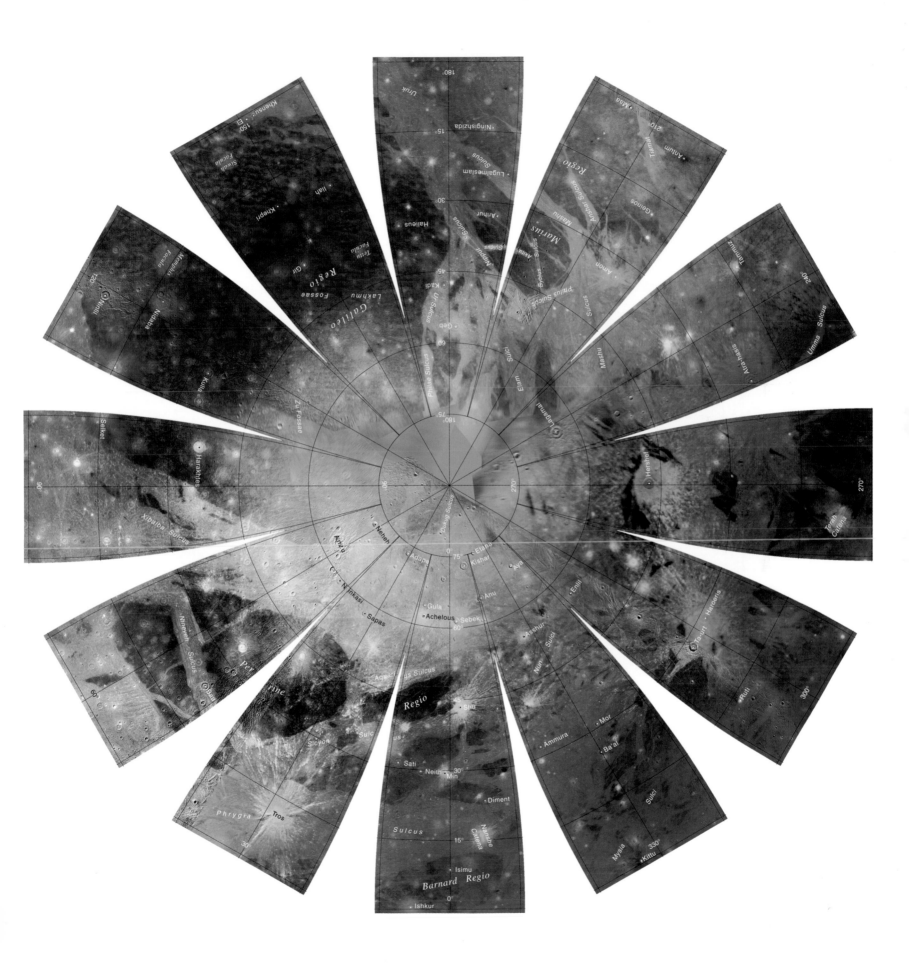

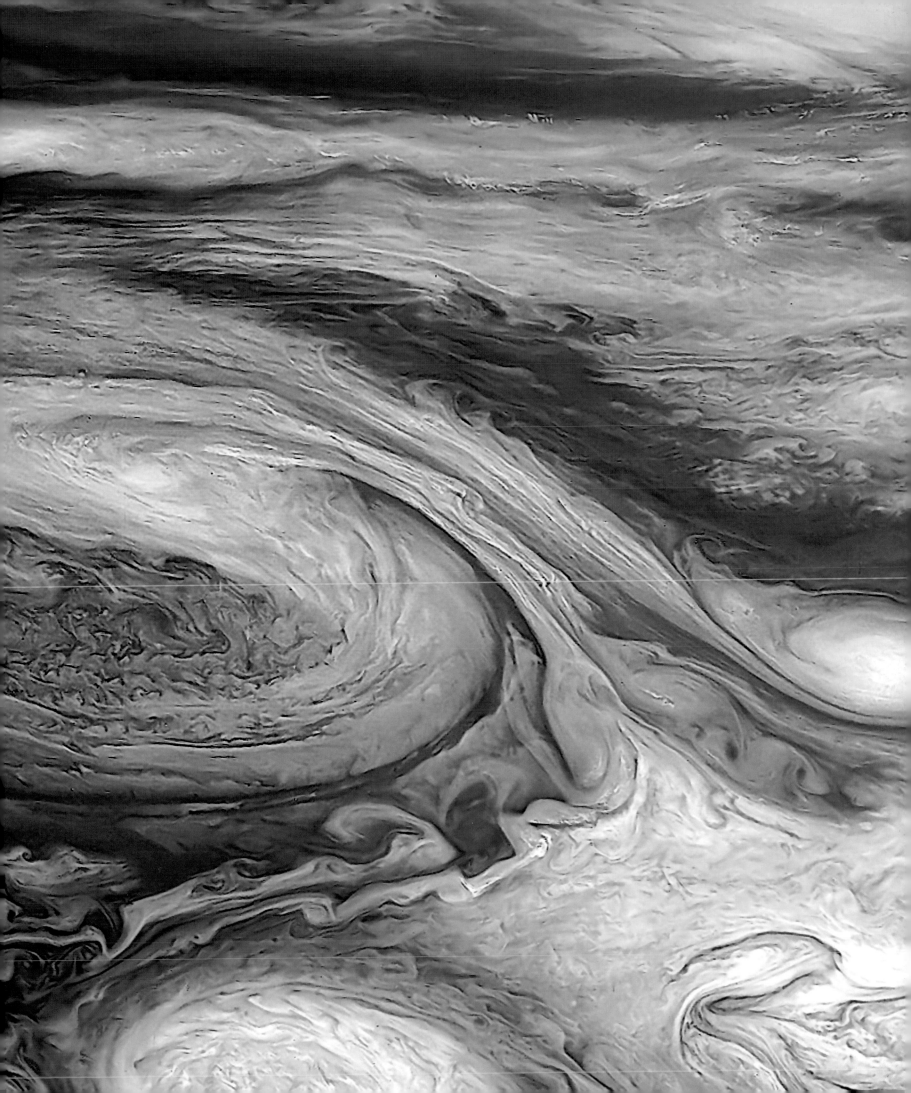

ON THE EDGE
OF THE TARANTULA

These fantastical shapes, silhouetted against an eerie background of green and blue are reminiscent of cavorting seahorses. Yet in fact these are mighty 'pillars of creation', many light years long, rising from a turbulent landscape of denser nebulosity some 100 light years across, in one of the largest and most active star-forming regions in our cosmic neighbourhood. This nebula, known as NGC 2074, lies on the outskirts of the much larger Tarantula Nebula in the Large Magellanic Cloud (LMC) – a satellite galaxy of our own Milky Way roughly 170,000 light years away.

Each dark tendril is held together by the gravity of protostars hidden within it – rapidly collapsing knots of gas and dust that will soon ignite into new stars and emerge from their present cocoons. Around them, thinner nebulosity is being driven back by a torrent of fierce ultraviolet radiation from previous generations of stellar newborns that now lie scattered across the nebula. The same invisible radiation excites atoms across the nebula and causes them to emit visible light at wavelengths linked to their atomic structure. In this Hubble Space Telescope image, taken at several specific wavelengths corresponding to chemical emissions within the nebula, red colours originate from sulphur and blue from oxygen, while green reveals the presence of hydrogen.

OBJECT **NGC 2074**

DISTANCE **170,000 light years**

RA **05h 39m 03s**

DEC **-69° 29' 38"**

OBSERVED WITH **Hubble Space Telescope**

Wide Field and Planetary Camera 2

BLUE MOON

Saturn's mid-sized satellite Dione looms out of ink-black space in this atmospheric enhanced-colour image from the Cassini spaceprobe. This view focuses principally on Dione's leading hemisphere – like our own Moon and most other satellites in the solar system, Dione is tidally locked so that one face is permanently turned towards Saturn, so one hemisphere also permanently faces forwards along the direction of its orbit.

Like most of Saturn's satellites, Dione is made from a mixture of rock and ice that allows its surface to slowly 'slump' over time. As a consequence, ancient craters across its surface have faded and only the most recent ones stand out. Curiously, Dione's trailing hemisphere is more heavily cratered than the leading one – the opposite of what we might expect, and evidence that Dione may have been spun round by one or more major impacts after the period of heaviest bombardment. In many places, craters seem to have been at least partly wiped away by eruptions of icy material from beneath the surface. Around the edges of Dione's visible face, oblique sunlight reveals the shadows of long parallel faults – features that dominate the satellite's other face. When first spotted by the Voyager spaceprobes in the early 1980s, these mysterious features were named 'wispy terrain'.

OBJECT **Dione**

SATELLITE OF **Saturn**

MIN DISTANCE **1.2 billion km (750 million miles)**

DIAMETER **1,122 km (697 miles)**

OBSERVED WITH **Cassini Imaging Science Subsystem**

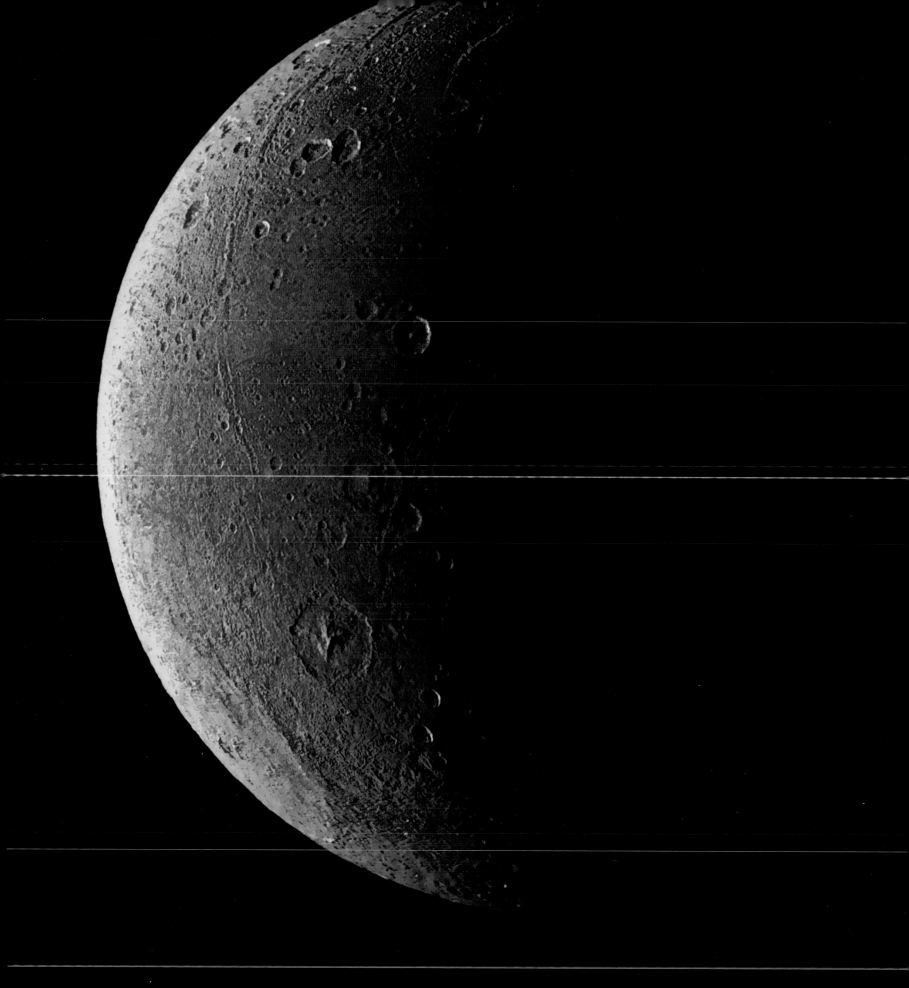

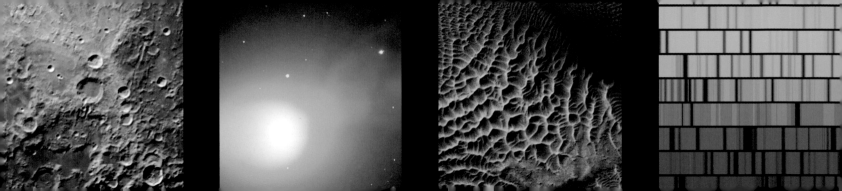

LIGHT AND
SHADOW

3

SATURN'S BLUES

The countless rings of Saturn cast their shadows across the planet's northern hemisphere in this atmospheric view from the Cassini spaceprobe as it passed just above the ring plane in May 2005. While Saturn's rings are divided by astronomers into a few distinct zones, each with a distinguishing letter, in reality each is composed of countless ringlets, and each of these is in turn made up of myriad tiny fragments in their own independent orbits around Saturn. When particles get out of line (tugged perhaps by tidal forces from Saturn's moons), jostling and collisions with their neighbours rapidly pushes them back in their place, ensuring the rings maintain their semblance of ordered calm. Differences in the appearance of the rings, meanwhile, are due to variations in the size, number and composition of the particles within them.

In this image, the planet and rings are lit from lower right, around southern midsummer. This side of the rings is largely unilluminated, glowing softly in scattered light from Saturn itself, but they cast prominent shadows across the planet. From the equator upwards, the fainter shadows come from the faint, semi-transparent D and C rings, while the broader and darker ones at higher latitudes correspond to the bright, dense B and A rings, separated by the prominent gap of the Cassini Division. Behind the ring shadows, the orb of Saturn grows notably bluer towards the north. This is due to the low angle of sunlight illuminating the northern hemisphere, and the scattering of that light as it passes through the rings.

OBJECT **Saturn**

MIN DISTANCE **1.2 billion km (750 million miles)**

DIAMETER **120,536 km (74,898 miles)**

OBSERVED WITH **Cassini Imaging Science Subsystem**

SOUTHERN DUNES

A variety of complex sand patterns ripple across the landscape in this intriguing image of a crater floor in the Noachis Terra region of the Martian southern hemisphere. While the northern regions of Mars are dominated by low rolling plains, the southern hemisphere is filled with far more chaotic and heavily cratered highlands that are thought to be rather older than their northern counterparts. Windblown sand accumulates in the floor of these craters, where it is frequently blown into beautiful dune patterns.

This image covers a region roughly 1 kilometre (0.6 miles) across, and shows countless small, crescent-shaped dunes around the foot of the larger hills, with linear ripples rising up their slopes. Mars displays some complicated dune structures unknown from Earth's deserts, which have long puzzled astronomers, but recent modelling suggests they may owe their unique forms to the small size of Martian sand grains (typically the size of house dust on Earth).

OBJECT **Mars**

MIN DISTANCE **54.6 million km**
(33.9 million miles)

DIAMETER **6,792 km (4,220 miles)**

OBSERVED WITH
Mars Reconnaissance Orbiter
High-Resolution Imaging
Science Experiment

➤ OPPOSITE

VEIL NEBULA

More than 5,000 years ago, a massive star exploded in the constellation of Cygnus, some 1,500 light years from Earth. Today, the shredded remnants of this supernova explosion are spread across some 70 light years of space, covering a region of Earth's sky roughly six times larger than the Full Moon.

The entire supernova remnant is called the Veil Nebula, and this, the brightest region within it, is known to astronomers as the Witch's Broom. Here, glowing gas piles up like waves breaking along a shoreline against a backdrop of crowded Milky Way starfields. The waves mark the path of an invisible shockwave, still expanding rapidly with the energy of the original stellar explosion, that is colliding with the surrounding interstellar medium and heating it to tremendous temperatures. The bright star near the centre of the image, known as 52 Cygni, is a foreground object at a distance of only 200 light years.

OBJECT **Veil Nebula, NGC 6960**

DISTANCE **1,500 light years**

RA **20h 45m 40s**

DEC **+30° 43' 11"**

OBSERVED WITH
Kitt Peak National Observatory
WIYN 0.9-m Telescope

➤➤ OVERLEAF

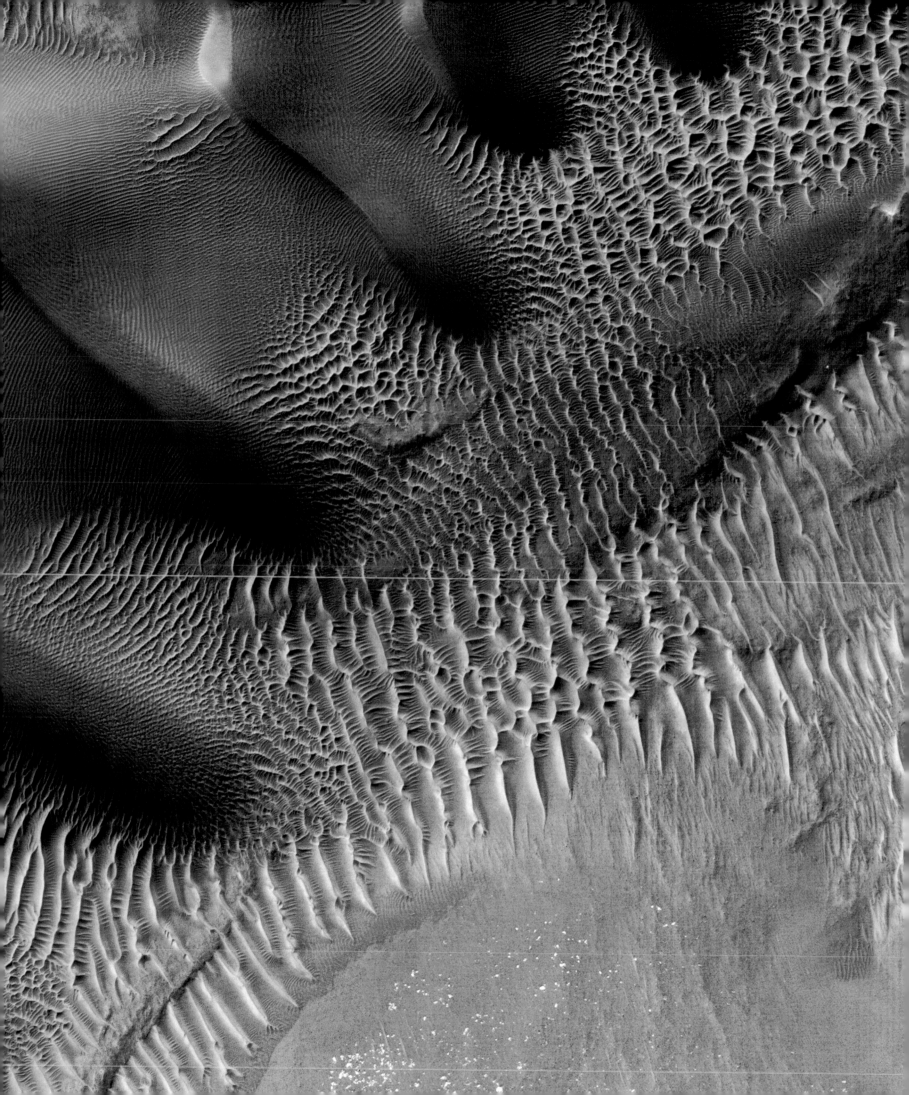

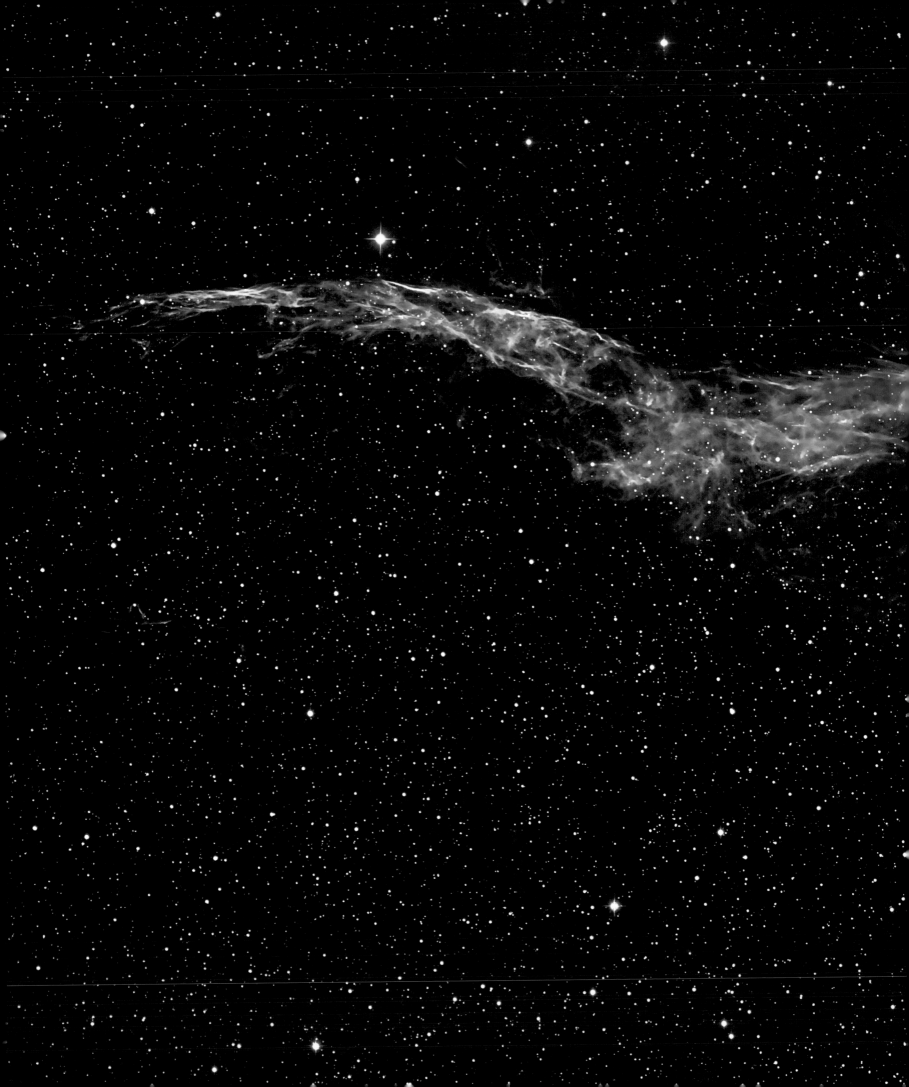

OVER THE LUNAR POLE

The searing heat of the Moon's daylit face shades into the impenetrable cold of lunar night across the airless cratered landscape of our satellite's north pole. This thought-provoking image was captured by NASA's Galileo spaceprobe in 1992 as it flew past Earth to pick up speed on its way to Jupiter. Because the Moon rotates in the same 27.3-day period it takes to circle the Earth, most places on the lunar surface experience a roughly equal day and night equivalent to 14 days each, during which midday temperatures reach 120°C (250°F) and night-time ones plummet to -200°C (-330°F).

In Galileo's view, the familiar *maria* or lunar seas (in reality, frozen lava plains) of the Moon's near side appear at the top, giving way to the heavily cratered, sealess landscape of the polar regions and far side towards the bottom. The lunar north pole itself is hidden in darkness at centre right, while the Humboldtianum Basin, a structure excavated by meteorite impacts and later partially filled in by lava, is at lower left.

An oddity of the Moon's orbit means it experiences no real seasons, and so polar regions are only ever illuminated by the Sun at a shallow angle. As a result, the floors of deep polar craters are sometimes lost in permanent shadow, and there is evidence (particularly at the south pole) that these contain substantial deposits of ice, dumped onto the Moon by the impact of comets.

OBJECT **The Moon**

MEAN DISTANCE **384,400 km (238,855 miles)**

DIAMETER **3,476 km (2,160 miles)**

OBSERVED WITH **Galileo Solid-State Imager**

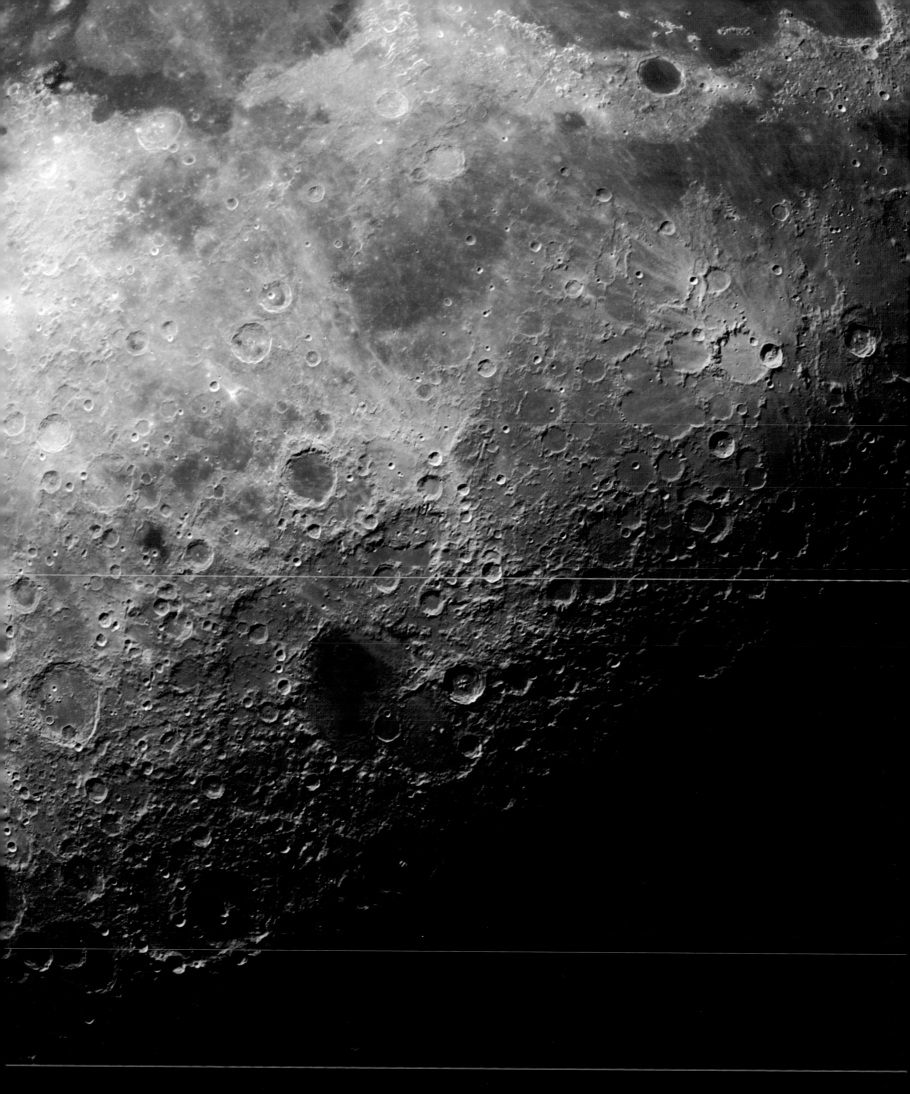

LUNAR ECLIPSE

Reminiscent of the grooves of a vinyl record, this unusual image captures the entirety of a lunar eclipse – a celestial spectacle in which the Full Moon passes through Earth's shadow over a period of several hours. The long-exposure view shows the motion of the stars and Moon through the sky as Earth rotates beneath them. The bright streak across the centre marks the passage of the Moon, dwindling from a blaze of light at either end to a narrow trail during mid-eclipse.

During a total eclipse, the Moon rarely disappears completely – Earth's atmosphere refracts sunlight passing around its edges, bending it to illuminate the Moon's darkened face. Because the atmosphere bends longer wavelengths in preference to shorter ones, the Moon usually takes on a bronze or blood-red tinge – it's only when large amounts of dust accumulate in Earth's atmosphere, for instance due to volcanic eruptions, that the Moon turns truly dark.

Because of Earth's size, the shadow it casts is considerably larger than the Moon's, and so a lunar eclipse requires a less precise alignment than a solar one. Furthermore, the eclipse is usually visible across the entire night side of our planet.

OBJECT **The Moon**

MEAN DISTANCE **384,400 km (238,855 miles)**

DIAMETER **3,476 km (2,160 miles)**

OBSERVED WITH **Amateur equipment (five-hour exposure)**

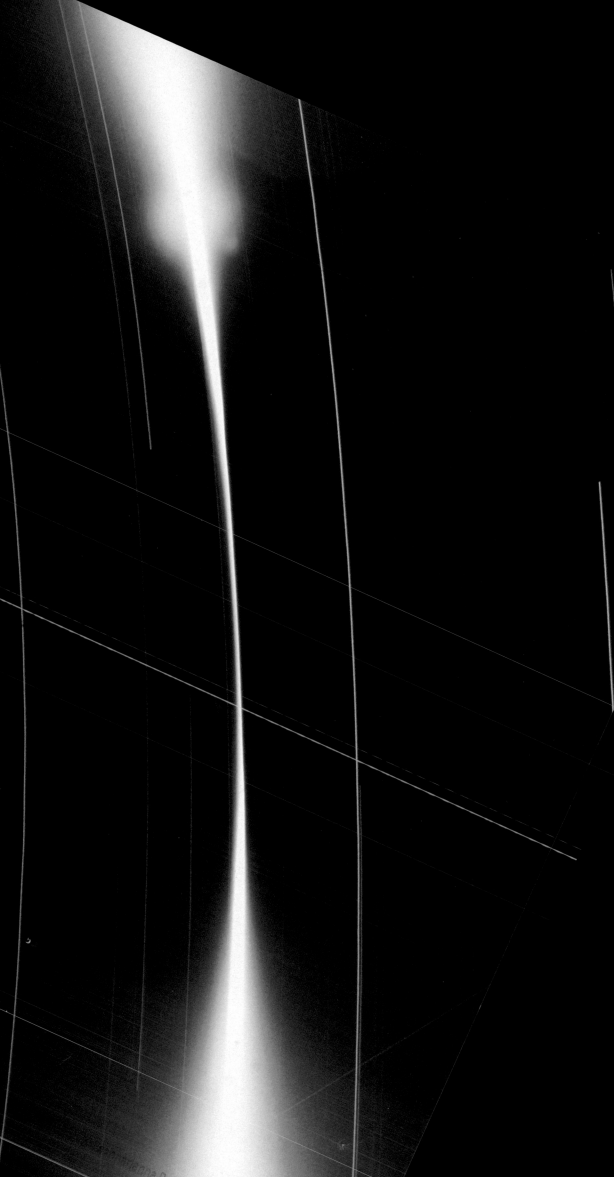

SOLAR SPECTRUM

This startling rainbow pattern is the chemical fingerprint of our Sun, a spectrum formed by splitting or 'diffracting' its light in different directions according to its wavelength. Captured using a spectrometer at the National Solar Observatory on Kitt Peak, Arizona, it covers the complete visible light output of our Sun, from the shortest violet wavelengths at the bottom, to the longest red ones at the top.

British scientist Isaac Newton first performed this experiment using a glass prism around 1670, discovering that the Sun's apparently pure light was actually made from a multitude of colours that are best explained by different wavelengths. One and a half centuries later, German optician Joseph von Fraunhöfer used more advanced equipment – a 'diffraction grating' that spreads out light by passing it through a series of narrow parallel slits – to create a more widely dispersed spectrum. Thanks to this technique, he discovered dark lines caused where light of specific wavelengths was being absorbed in the solar atmosphere.

Later in the 19th century, German scientists Robert Bunsen and Gustav Kirchoff discovered that burning laboratory chemicals produced light at similarly narrow wavelengths, and absorbed light from a 'continuum' at the same wavelengths. Furthermore, each element or chemical compound displayed a unique pattern of 'spectral lines' linked to its subatomic structure. This was the origin of spectroscopy, the technique of analyzing a celestial object's chemical make-up from its spectrum.

OBJECT **The Sun**

MEAN DISTANCE **149.6 million km (93 million miles)**

DIAMETER **1.392 million km (865,000 miles)**

OBSERVED WITH **Kitt Peak National Solar Observatory**

McMath-Pierce Solar Facility

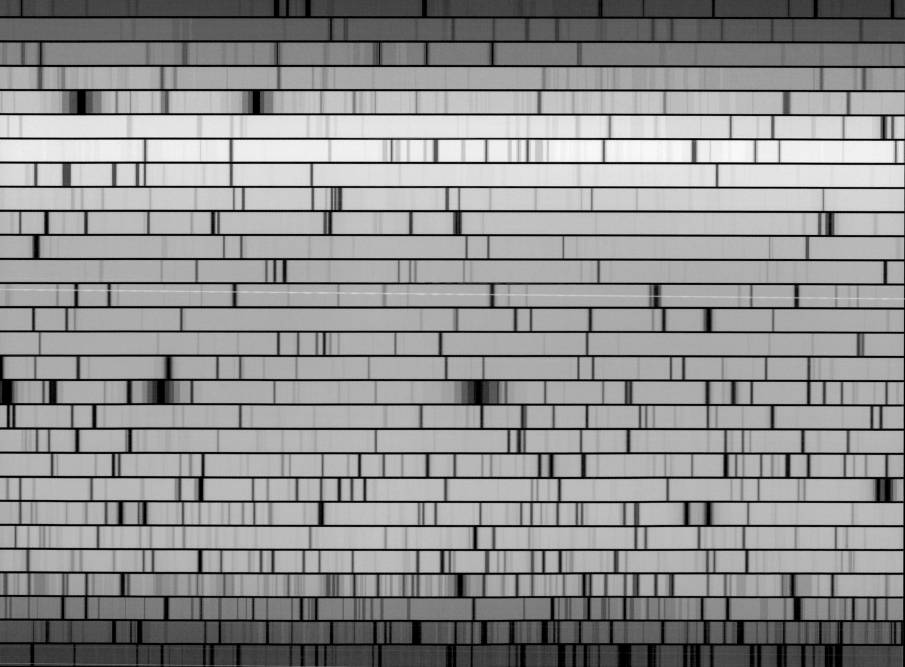

BLOSSOMING NEBULA

The Great Orion Nebula erupts in full bloom, an example of nature's artistry at its finest, in this astonishing image from the Hubble Space Telescope. The nebula is the brightest in Earth's skies, clearly visible to the naked eye in the 'sword' of the bright constellation of Orion the Hunter. Seen through Hubble's crystal-clear optics, it resolves into two distinct regions, the large, flower-like Messier 42 and the smaller, roughly circular Messier 43 (at upper left in this image). Both are around 1,500 light years from Earth. To create this stunning mosaic, Hubble scientists pieced together data from 520 separate images at five separate wavelengths, including the near-infrared, which reveals objects too cool to shine in visible light.

A renowned cluster of bright newly formed stars nestles at the heart of Messier 42, known as the Trapezium on account of the shape formed by its four brightest stars. Radiation from this cluster illuminates the interior of the cavern-shaped star-forming region, through a mixture of direct reflection (seen in the bluer areas) and excitation (shown where pinkish areas fluoresce under exposure to ultraviolet light). Stellar winds, meanwhile, are carving out the cavern from inside, creating the intricate ripples seen to either side of the central cluster. Red stars in the lower half of the nebula are lightweight 'brown dwarfs', too faint to be seen in visible light, while to the right side of the image, young stars that are already escaping the nebula create glowing shockwaves as their own stellar winds collide with the surrounding interstellar medium.

OBJECT **Orion Nebula, M42**

DISTANCE **1,500 light years**

RA **05h 35m 17s**

DEC **-05° 23' 28"**

OBSERVED WITH **Hubble Space Telescope**

Advanced Camera for Surveys

WHIRLPOOL GALAXY

In one of the sharpest images ever recorded from the depths of space, the graceful spiral of the celebrated Whirlpool Galaxy is picked out in the blue brilliance of open clusters and the pinkish glow of star formation. The Whirlpool, also known as Messier 51, is one of the brightest and best-defined spiral galaxies in Earth's skies, located about 31 million light years away in the northern constellation of Canes Venatici.

This Hubble Space Telescope image reveals the true complexities of the Whirlpool and its relationship to the smaller nearby galaxy NGC 5195. Astronomers had previously thought that the smaller galaxy was colliding with the larger one, and connected directly to it by the spiral arm at top left. However, it's now clear that in reality, NGC 5195 is actually passing behind the Whirlpool. Nevertheless, the smaller galaxy is still exerting a considerable influence – as its gravity tugs at the individual orbits of objects within the disc, it pulls them into a spiral 'density wave' rather like the short-term clustering of cars passing through a traffic jam. Stars, gas and dust passing through the wave region are compressed, triggering new waves of star formation that eventually release brilliant young star clusters that highlight the spiral pattern. By the time their long, slow orbits have carried these clusters out of the density wave, the brightest stars in these clusters will already have aged and disappeared in supernova explosions, while the rest of the stars will become increasingly scattered amid the multitude of stars in the galaxy's disc.

OBJECT **Whirlpool Galaxy, M51**

DISTANCE **31 million light years**

RA **13h 29m 53s**

DEC **+47° 11' 41"**

OBSERVED WITH **Hubble Space Telescope Advanced Camera for Surveys**

HORSEHEAD NEBULA

The elegant shape of a horse's head, sculpted from a dark pillar of dust and silhouetted against a curtain of glowing gases, forms an unmistakable centrepiece to this view of nebulosity around Orion's Belt. The horsehead is the most famous of all dark nebulae, but its distinctive chess-piece shape is only a brief phase in its ongoing evolution. The nebula lies around 1,500 light years from Earth and is roughly two light years across at its head. Like the famous 'Pillars of Creation' found elsewhere in our galaxy (see page 108), it is in the process of collapsing to form new stars.

Beyond the horsehead lies the softly glowing emission nebula IC 434. This shimmering screen of light is composed largely of hydrogen, fluorescing under ultraviolet light from the nearby bright star Sigma Orionis. The nebula's striated appearance is caused by the weak magnetic field of the Milky Way itself. At far left in this image lies the bright star Alnitak. Beneath it lies the Flame Nebula, NGC 2024, appearing very different in visible light than it does in an infrared view (see page 26).

OBJECT **Horsehead Nebula, Barnard 33**
DISTANCE **1,500 light years**
RA **05h 40m 59s**
DEC **-02° 27' 30"**
OBSERVED WITH
European Southern Observatory
Visible and Infrared Survey Telescope
for Astronomy

➤ OPPOSITE

CARINA'S INFRARED LANDSCAPE

This dramatic view displays an array of features in the Carina Nebula, NGC 3372. Using the HAWK-I near-infrared camera and the Very Large Telescope at Paranal, Chile, astronomers lifted the veil of dust in the foreground of the nebula in order to reveal the intricate structures within.

Although the nebula is best known as one of the Milky Way's most impressive regions of star formation, it is also destined to become a stellar graveyard. The brilliant star at lower left is Eta Carinae, a system of two heavyweight stars that are hurtling towards their deaths in supernova explosions. The twin stars of Eta were born just a few million years ago, but thanks to their enormous mass, they have burnt through their nuclear fuel very rapidly and are now becoming unstable as they age. Elsewhere in the image, dark tendrils and isolated clouds mark areas where new stars are being born, while a brilliant multicoloured star cluster, known as Trumpler 14, glitters like a stellar jewel box at the centre of the picture.

OBJECT **Carina Nebula, NGC 3372**
DISTANCE **7,500 light years**
RA **10h 45m 09s**
DEC **-59° 52' 04"**
OBSERVED WITH
European Southern Observatory
Very Large Telescope HAWK-I Camera

➤➤ OVERLEAF

SOMBRERO GALAXY

A broad, dark rim of dust hems the edge of a bright galactic platter in this beautiful image of an iconic but puzzling galaxy. Catalogued as Messier 104, the Sombrero lies in the galaxy-packed constellation of Virgo – but at a relatively nearby 28 million light years, it is a lot closer than most members of the famous Virgo Cluster.

Based on visible-light photographs such as this one from the European Southern Observatory, astronomers have long considered the Sombrero to be a fairly normal spiral galaxy with a particularly large central bulge and an unusually prominent dust lane. However, recent observations at other wavelengths have shown that this is only half the story. X-ray observations show a host of high-energy X-ray sources such as black holes scattered in a broad halo above and below the disc, while infrared views, which can pierce the Sombrero's dust and are more sensitive to the light of old, cool stars, confirm that there is much more matter distributed in a broad spherical halo around the visible galaxy. In fact, it now appears that the distribution of stars is more like that found in spherical giant elliptical galaxies than that seen in typical spirals.

So the Sombrero galaxy seems to be a rare hybrid – an elliptical galaxy with a well-defined disc of brighter stars and dust embedded within it. Precisely how this fits into our picture of galactic evolution is a question that remains to be answered.

OBJECT **Sombrero Galaxy, M104**

DISTANCE **28 million light years**

RA **12h 39m 59s**

DEC **-11° 37' 23"**

OBSERVED WITH **European Southern Observatory**
1.5-m Danish Telescope

TWO SIDES OF A RING SYSTEM

This unusual image captures a remarkable moment of contrast in the rings of Saturn, as the planet's deep shadow slices across the delicate ringlets, plunging them from light into darkness. Saturn's ring system produces some remarkably sophisticated arrangements of lighting, and NASA's Cassini spaceprobe, in orbit around the planet since 2004, has photographed many of them. In this particular view from 2009, Cassini is looking down from above the ring plane onto the unilluminated northern side of the rings, and beyond them to the orb of Saturn itself.

At upper left, Saturn's northern hemisphere shines dimly in light scattered through the rings, while the southern hemisphere is illuminated by reflected sunlight from the brighter side of the rings, creating a broad curving swathe of bright twilight.

In the lower half of the image, sunlight scattered among the ring particles lights up their illuminated side, revealing an array of ringlets of varying width and density, while in the upper right quadrant, the rings are plunged into shadow and can only be seen where they are silhouetted against the twilight of the southern hemisphere. Bright points of light among the rings, meanwhile, are in fact distant stars passing behind them.

OBJECT **Saturn**

MIN DISTANCE **1.2 billion km (750 million miles)**

DIAMETER **120,536 km (74,898 miles)**

OBSERVED WITH **Cassini Imaging Science Subsystem**

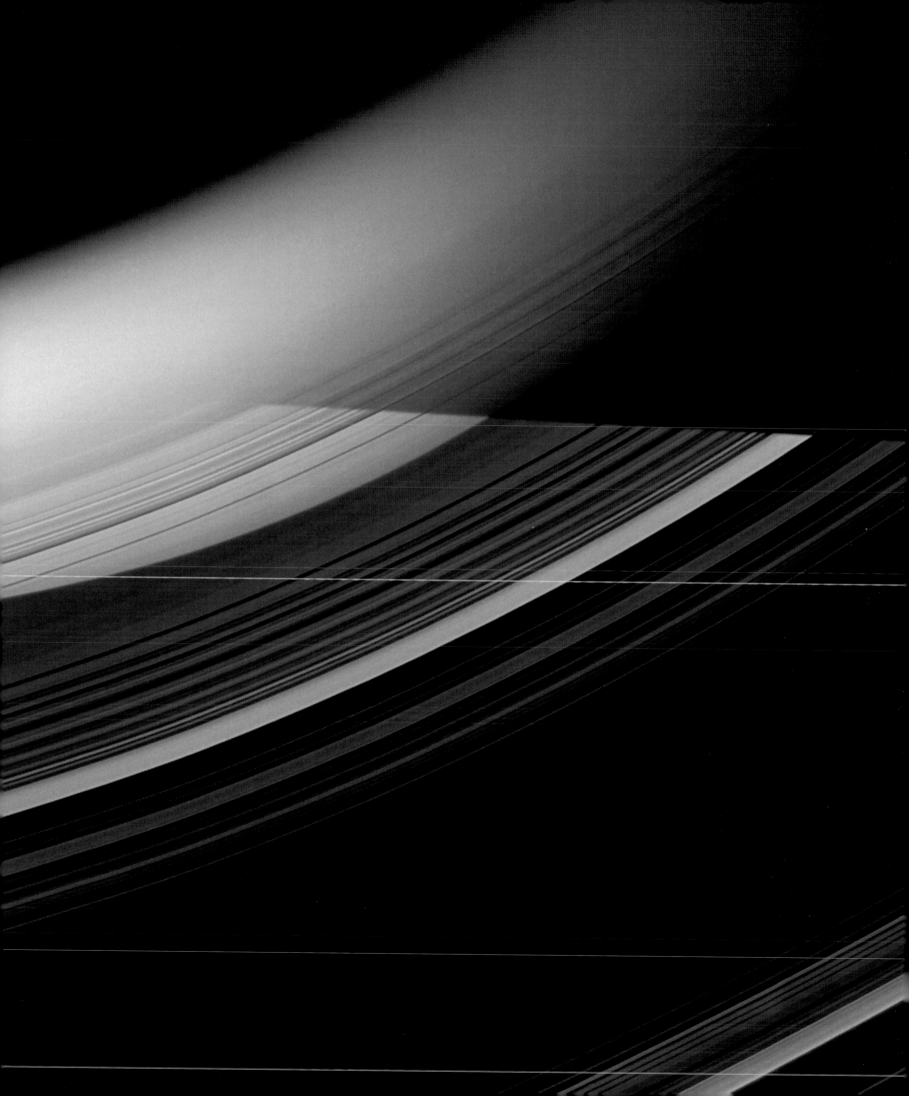

CELESTIAL SPIRE

Some see the figure of an angel perched on a pinnacle in this diaphanous pillar of dust and gas. More widely, however, the structure is known as 'the Spire'. It lies 6,500 light years away at the heart of the Eagle Nebula, one of the most intensely studied regions of star formation. This nebula (see page 136) shot to fame after observations from the Hubble Space Telescope revealed the first detailed views of its complex star-forming regions, soon nicknamed the 'Pillars of Creation'. The spire marks the eroded remains of one such pillar, racing to complete the processes of starbirth before it is blown away completely in a torrent of fierce radiation from bright stars beyond the top of the picture. The glowing background is caused by more distant gas clouds fluorescing in ultraviolet light – near the top, blue reveals the presence of oxygen, while towards the base, red shows hydrogen-rich regions.

The upper reaches of the spire, shown here, are roughly four light years long. Dark knots within them, and finger-like extrusions around the edges, mark locations where stars are trying to form, although some are being rapidly snuffed out by the dwindling supplies of material. The recent discovery of an expanding shockwave from a supernova explosion some 6,000 years ago suggests that time is running out for the pillars – in the next few thousand years, we may see them torn apart as the shockwave rips through them.

OBJECT **Eagle Nebula, Messier 16**

DISTANCE **6,500 light years**

RA **18h 18m 51s**

DEC **-13° 49' 51"**

OBSERVED WITH **Hubble Space Telescope**

Advanced Camera for Surveys

CANNIBAL
SILHOUETTE

A dramatic Hubble Space Telescope image extends beyond the limits of visible light to reveal hidden features in the heart of active galaxy NGC 5128, also known as Centaurus A. This intriguing system, 11 million light years from Earth in the southern constellation of Centaurus, is thought to mark a recent galactic merger in which a large elliptical galaxy has absorbed a smaller spiral and is now cannibalizing its material, including the broad band of dust that runs across its more or less spherical face.

The collision has sparked a firestorm of starbirth within NGC 5128 – shockwaves compressing gas clouds around the site of the impact have triggered rapid star formation, highlighted by the intense pink glow of excited hydrogen. Hubble's near-ultraviolet vision has pierced the dust cloud in places to reveal compact open star clusters, dominated by hot stars that have already been released by previous waves of starbirth. These are shown as intense blue-white spots within the image.

OBJECT **Centaurus A, NGC 5128**

DISTANCE **11 million light years**

RA **13h 25m 28s**

DEC **-43° 01' 09"**

OBSERVED WITH

Hubble Space Telescope

Wide Field Camera 3

➤ OPPOSITE

STRANGE VISITOR

This eerie interloper among the stars is Comet Lulin, discovered by astronomers from the University of Taiwan's Lulin Observatory in July 2007 and photographed when at its brightest in Earth's skies during February 2009. Comets are small icy objects, mostly in remote elliptical orbits around the Sun. As they enter the inner solar system and are warmed by solar radiation, the ices within them begin to evaporate, forming first a thin but extensive atmosphere known as the coma, and then one or more elongated tails.

The most prominent tail is usually formed as particles from the solar wind blow gases away from the comet and ionize them, making the tail glow. This ion tail always points in a straight line away from the Sun, but a comet may also display dust tails that shine by reflected sunlight and tend to curve along the comet's direction of travel. Finally, a spike-like 'anti-tail' is sometimes created by heavier escaping dust trapped in orbit in front of the comet's central nucleus. Lulin displayed a particularly prominent anti-tail, which dominates this picture.

OBJECT **Comet Lulin**

MIN DISTANCE **61.5 million km**

(38.2 million miles)

ORBITAL PERIOD **42,000 years**

OBSERVED WITH **Amateur equipment**

➤➤ OVERLEAF

VISIBLE AND INVISIBLE

4

HELIX NEBULA

A baleful celestial eye stares out of the cosmic darkness in this spectacular image, a composite of observations from the Hubble Space Telescope's Advanced Camera for Surveys and the ground-based 4-metre (160-in) telescope at Chile's Cerro Tololo Inter-American Observatory.

The Helix Nebula, NGC 7293, is one of the closest and brightest planetary nebulae to Earth – the expanding remains of a dying Sun-like star that has shed its outer layers into space. At an estimated 700 light years away and around 2.5 light years across, it appears just slightly smaller than the Full Moon in Earth's skies. However, its structure is enigmatic – astronomers have used this image to show that the nebula consists of two discs of gas – the bright inner one face-on to Earth, and a larger, faint outer one (the dim orange clouds in this image). The outer ring surrounds the inner one, and is tilted close to edge-on from our point of view. The origins of these two interlocking discs is uncertain, but one possibility is that they are influenced by the presence of an unseen companion star orbiting close to the star that is actually shedding the gas.

The Helix was the first planetary nebula to reveal 'cometary knots' – radial streaks that have nothing to do with comets themselves, but are in fact created when fast-moving shells of gas expelled towards the end of the nebula's formation catch up and collide with slower-moving, denser gas ejected in earlier times.

OBJECT **Helix Nebula, NGC 7293**

DISTANCE **700 light years**

RA **22h 29m 39s**

DEC **-20° 50' 14"**

OBSERVED WITH **Hubble Space Telescope Advanced Camera for Surveys,**
Cerro Tololo Inter-American Observatory 4-m Telescope

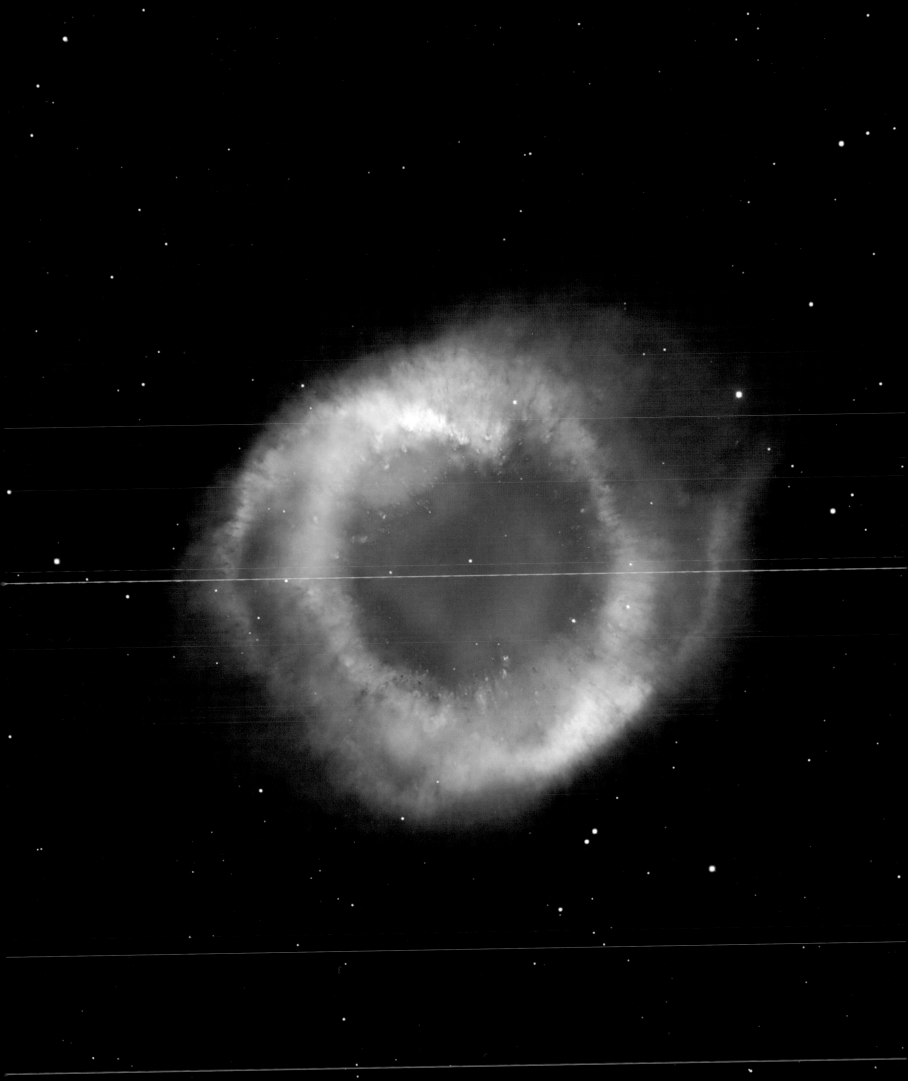

BUBBLE NEBULA

A perfect soap bubble in space makes an incongruous sight, afloat on a limpid pool amid the Milky Way starfields of Cassiopeia. Catalogued as NGC 7635, the Bubble Nebula encloses a massive star about 7,000 light years from Earth.

The Bubble was discovered by German-British astronomer William Herschel in 1787, and is created as a stellar wind blowing off the surface of the central star, known as BD+602522, slams into the surrounding nebula and triggers glowing emission. BD+602522 has an estimated mass of about 40 Suns and a hot, blue-white surface. Its stellar winds start out at speeds of around 7 million kilometres per hour (4 million mph), but slow dramatically as they encounter the denser surroundings.

Close-up views of the Bubble's surface reveal a rippled appearance, created as density differences in the surrounding material slow down the shockwave at different points, and the central star is noticeably offset from the centre of the Bubble for similar reasons. The entire Bubble is about six light years across, and is just the brightest of three roughly concentric shells of gas – a larger outer one has already begun to fade and merge with the surrounding nebula, while a small inner one is now developing. Beyond the outermost shell, the star's fierce radiation has carved out a cavern within the surrounding nebulosity, which glows from within as it is excited by ultraviolet light.

OBJECT **Bubble Nebula, NGC 7635**

DISTANCE **7,000 light years**

RA **23h 20m 48s**

DEC **+61° 12' 06"**

OBSERVED WITH **Kitt Peak National Observatory**

WIYN 3.5-m Telescope

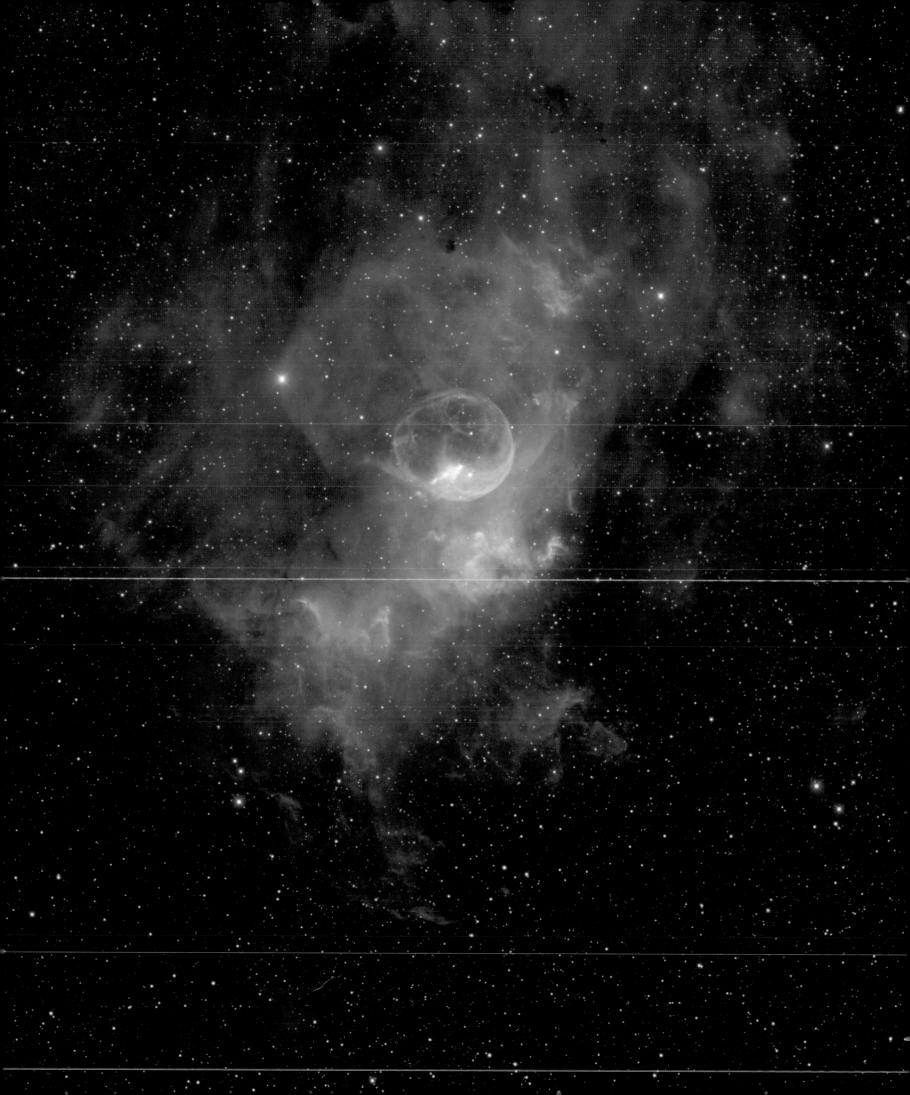

INFRARED ORION

The famous Great Orion Nebula glows with hitherto invisible light in this extraordinary panorama from the European Southern Observatory's Visible and Infrared Survey Telescope for Astronomy (VISTA). The brightest and closest major region of star formation, the Great Nebula lies around 1,500 light years from Earth and is the brightest part of a large and mostly invisible hydrogen cloud, the Orion Molecular Complex. The Hubble Space Telescope is just one of many instruments to have captured stunning details of the nebula in visible light (see page 96).

Near-infrared observations from VISTA detect radiation from regions too cool to shine in visible light – even ones that lie behind opaque dust clouds – and as a result the already spectacular nebula explodes into vibrant life. The VISTA image shows glowing gas clouds all the way along the chain of stars that forms Orion's sword.

The Trapezium star cluster of bright stars at the heart of the Great Nebula itself is lost in this blaze of light, but other previously unknown stars come into view scattered across the nebula. Small red clouds above the central region, meanwhile, are thought to mark newly formed stars that are still hidden from view inside dusty cocoons, but are flinging out streams of high-energy gas that heat up their surroundings. According to some models, the ejected matter could be moving at speeds of up to 700,000 kilometres per hour (435,000 mph).

OBJECT **Orion Nebula, M42**

DISTANCE **1,500 light years**

RA **05h 35m 17s**

DEC **-05° 23' 28"**

OBSERVED WITH **European Southern Observatory**
Visible and Infrared Survey Telescope for Astronomy

ON THE SHORES OF
THE LAGOON

Delicate waves of gas ripple across light years of space, recalling an impressionistic seascape in this Hubble Space Telescope view of the Lagoon Nebula in Sagittarius. The Lagoon, also known as Messier 8, is among the largest and brightest star-forming nebulae in Earth's skies. Discovered by French astronomer Guillaume Le Gentil in 1747, it is one of the few such nebulae that can be seen with the naked eye under dark skies, covering an area roughly three times the width of the Full Moon.

The Lagoon lies around 4,000 light years from Earth, and covers an area about 140 x 60 light years across. It takes its name from a broad dust stream that runs across its centre, but is outside the field of view of this image. Although the nebula is excited by radiation from the young stars within, it is only in recent times that astronomers have confirmed the presence of ongoing starbirth within dark, star-forming pillars and globules.

In this false-colour image, taken using Hubble's Advanced Camera for Surveys, visible light collected through a yellow filter is tinted blue, while light emitted by glowing hydrogen at specific wavelengths is coloured red and emissions from nitrogen are coloured green.

OBJECT **Lagoon Nebula, M8**

DISTANCE **4,000 light years**

RA **18h 03m 37s**

DEC **-24° 23' 12"**

OBSERVED WITH **Hubble Space Telescope**

Advanced Camera for Surveys

THE LABYRINTH
OF NIGHT

An array of colourful streaks and fractal patterns dominate this false-colour view of a single junction within the Noctis Labyrinthus, an extension of the enormous Valles Marineris canyon system on Mars.

The Valles Marineris or Mariner Valleys (named for the Mariner 9 spacecraft that discovered them in 1971) form the grandest canyon in the solar system. This vast crack in the Martian surface runs for more than 4,000 kilometres (2,450 miles) and is up to 10 kilometres (6 miles) deep in places. It is believed to have split open as a result of pressure created during the build-up of the Tharsis Rise, the volcanic 'bulge' that underlies many of the planet's major volcanoes (see page 170). The romantically named Noctis Labyrinthus or 'Labyrinth of Night' is a maze-like system of smaller valleys between the Tharsis Rise and the main canyon, formed by faults linked to volcanic activity.

In this image from the Thermal Emission Imaging System (THEMIS) on board NASA's Mars Odyssey spaceprobe, colour coding reveals temperature variations on the Martian surface around a depression some 4,000 metres (13,000 ft) deep. Cooler areas, shown in blue, are linked to accumulations of dust, while warmer areas in yellow and red show exposed rock.

OBJECT **Mars**

MIN DISTANCE **54.6 million km**
(33.9 million miles)

DIAMETER **6,792 km (4,220 miles)**

OBSERVED WITH **Mars Odyssey Thermal**
Emission Imaging System

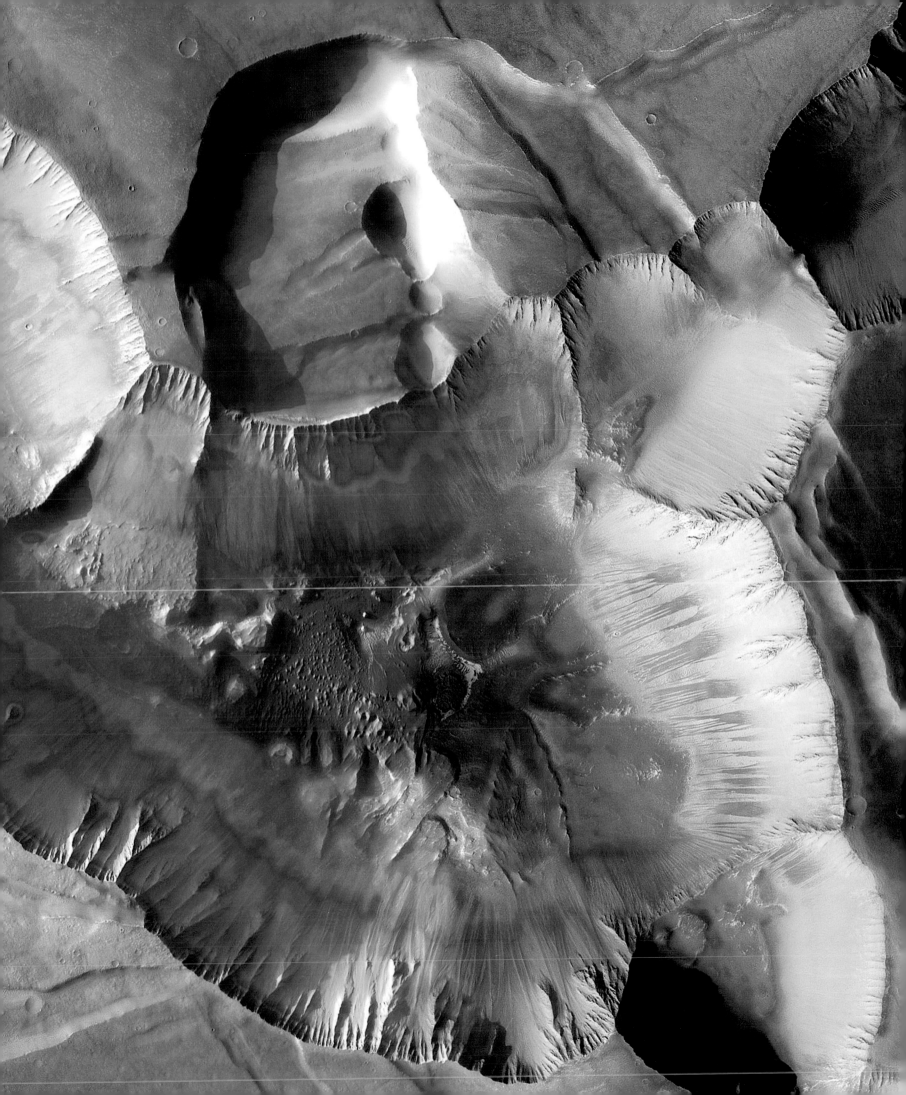

AFLOAT IN THE NIGHT

Pale blue gas clouds billow like the sails of a cosmic ship around NGC 346, an open star cluster so bright that it is prominent even over intergalactic distances. NGC 346 is the largest star-formation region in the Small Magellanic Cloud, a satellite galaxy in orbit around the Milky Way, around 210,000 light years from Earth. It contains an estimated 2,500 infant stars, surrounded by a cloud of raw stellar ingredients designated N66.

Hubble's sharp vision identified the chain of dust clouds near the bottom of the image as the focus of ongoing starbirth within the nebula. Analysis of more than 70,000 stars in the region shows that the nebula has gone through at least three waves of starbirth. The oldest dates back to around 4.5 billion years ago (at around the same time as the Sun itself was forming), and its stars have long since drifted out of the nebula's core. The most recent wave, in contrast, seems to have begun just 5 million years ago.

The heavyweight, bright and fast-burning stars from earlier generations have long since burnt out. They destroyed themselves in supernova explosions that scattered the atomic material processed during their lifetimes back into the nebula. As a result, later generations of stars are enriched with heavier elements, and burn brighter and faster. It is the radiation and stellar winds from these stars that now sculpt their fantastical surroundings.

OBJECT **NGC 346**

DISTANCE **210,000 light years**

RA **0h 59m 18s**

DEC **-72° 10' 48"**

OBSERVED WITH **Hubble Space Telescope**

Advanced Camera for Surveys

CAT'S PAW NEBULA

The large, star-forming NGC 6334 covers an area slightly larger than the Full Moon, amid the dense Milky Way star clouds of the constellation Scorpius. The multi-lobed shape formed by its main components has given rise to its common names of the Bear Claw and the Cat's Paw.

This image, captured at La Silla Observatory in Chile, covers only the brightest regions of an object some 50 light years wide in total. Large quantities of interstellar dust in the 5,500 light years between Earth and the Cat's Paw scatter short wavelengths of light towards the blue end of the spectrum and give the nebula its intensely red appearance. This is thought to be one of the most active star-forming regions in the Milky Way at present. Newborn giants, many times the mass of the Sun, are responsible for most of the ultraviolet radiation that makes the hydrogen clouds fluoresce, but these are just the most prominent among many thousands of stars concealed amid the nebula's gas and dust.

OBJECT **Cat's Paw Nebula, NGC 6334**

DISTANCE **5,500 light years**

RA **17h 19m 58s**

DEC **-35° 57' 47"**

OBSERVED WITH

European Southern Observatory

MPG/ESO 2.2-m Telescope

➤ OPPOSITE

HEART OF THE MILKY WAY

Some 26,000 light years and countless intervening clouds of stars, gas and dust separate Earth from the core of our galaxy. In visible light it is totally hidden from our view behind the bright star clouds of Sagittarius. Orbiting telescopes that observe at other wavelengths of radiation, however, can pierce the veil, revealing a strange landscape of twisted dust clouds, violent stars and superhot gas.

Perhaps the most important feature in this chaotic region is the bright X-ray source (shown in blue-white) to the right of centre. This is a huge cluster of heavyweight stars swimming in a sea of hot gas, surrounding the exact centre of the Milky Way. The centre itself, marked by an object known as Sagittarius A*, is invisible at all wavelengths except for radio waves. However, its gravitational influence shows that it contains the mass of at least 4 million Suns in a space smaller than Uranus's orbit. The only object that can possibly contain such a density of matter is a supermassive black hole – a region of space with such powerful gravity that even light cannot escape its clutches.

OBJECT **Sagittarius A, Milky Way Galaxy**

DISTANCE **26,000 light years**

RA **17h 45m 40s**

DEC **-29° 00' 28"**

OBSERVED WITH

Hubble Space Telescope Near-Infrared Camera and Multi-Object Spectrometer, Chandra X-Ray Observatory, Spitzer Space Telescope

➤ ➤ OVERLEAF

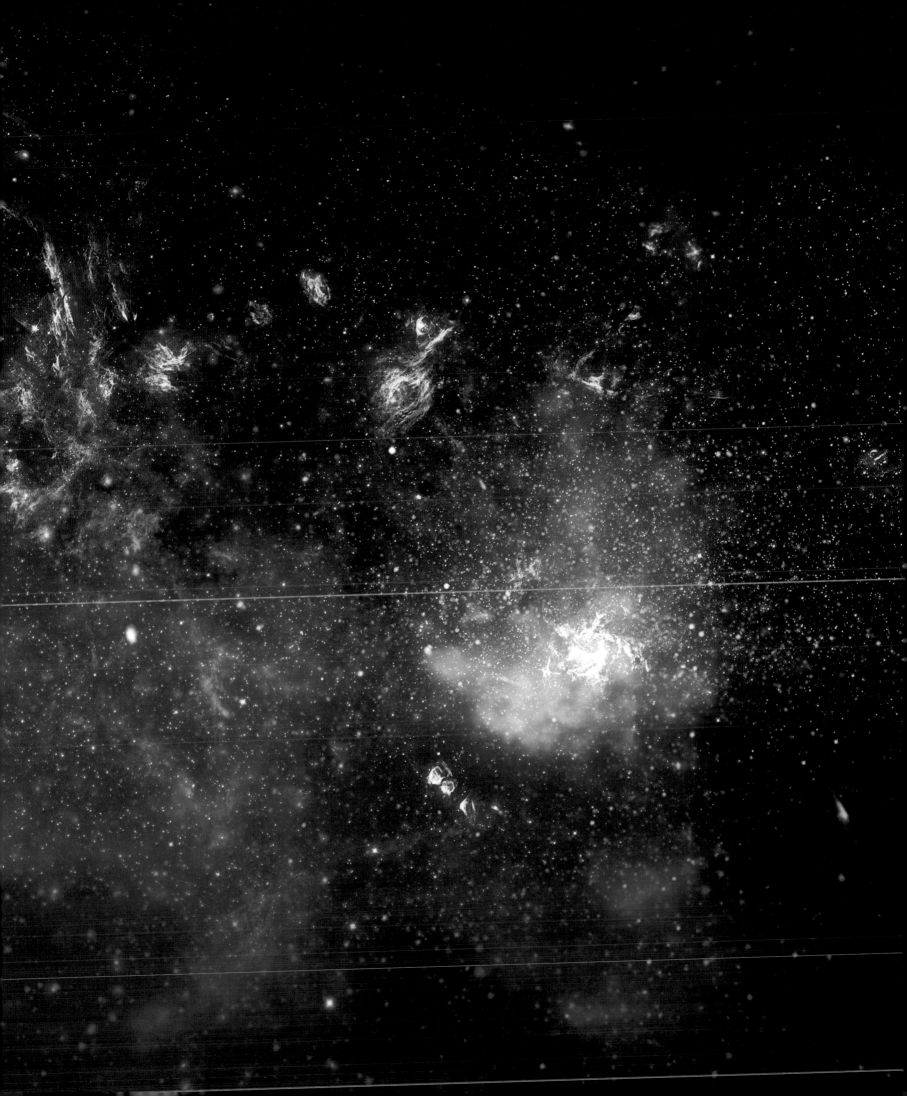

COSMIC SKULL

The unsettling sight of a ghostly death's head appears to stare back from this image of the region around star cluster NGC 2467. A small knot of stars, known as Haffner 19, marks the position of one eye and a single bright star the other, each sitting neatly in the socket of opaque dust. Little wonder, then, that astronomers nickname this cluster the Skull and Crossbones.

But look beyond the superficial resemblance and this beautiful image from the European Southern Observatory's 2.2-metre (88-in) telescope at La Silla Observatory, Chile, becomes a symphony in pink and green. At the centre of the image, framed in a junction of dark dust streams, lies the cluster Haffner 18, whose hot young stars provide much of the ultraviolet radiation that excites the surrounding gas and causes it to glow.

Haffner 18 and its associated nebulosity lie around 28,000 light years away from Earth, in the southern constellation of Puppis, the Stern (formerly part of the great celestial ship Argo). At the centre of the large, pink-fringed region towards the bottom of the image sits the bright young star HD 64315, whose fierce radiation and stellar winds are helping to shape the entire region.

OBJECT **NGC 2467**

DISTANCE **28,000 light years**

RA **07h 52m 30s**

DEC **-26° 25' 48"**

OBSERVED WITH **European Southern Observatory**

MPG/ESO 2.2-m Telescope

CAT'S EYE NEBULA

A dying star wraps itself in a spiral cocoon of gas and dust in this entrancing image from the Hubble Space Telescope. The Cat's Eye Nebula, NGC 6543, is one of the most celebrated planetary nebulae, around 3,300 light years from Earth in the northern constellation of Draco. The complex interlocking structures at the centre of the nebula are created by expanding bubbles of gas, inflated from within by strong winds of X-ray emitting particles blown off the surface of the central star. The bubbles are pinched at the 'waist' by a slowly expanding disc of denser material above the star's equator. However, the central axis of the system seems to have changed over time, probably tugged in various directions by an unseen companion to the central star. Beyond this inner region lies a system of concentric rings – a series of shells released when the star underwent a period of regular pulsations between 15,000 and 1,000 years ago.

Even further out, beyond the limits of this image, the entire system is surrounded by shredded clouds of material, released in a less orderly outburst thousands of years before the present nebula appeared, when the central star was still an unstable red giant. Planetary nebulae are rapidly evolving objects, and the current centre of the Cat's Eye has developed in just the past few centuries. In another few millennia, its glowing gases will cool and fade, while the surviving stellar remnant will sink into obscurity as a faint white dwarf star.

OBJECT **Cat's Eye Nebula, NGC 6543**

DISTANCE **3,300 light years**

RA **17h 58m 34s**

DEC **+66° 37' 59"**

OBSERVED WITH **Hubble Space Telescope**

Advanced Camera for Surveys

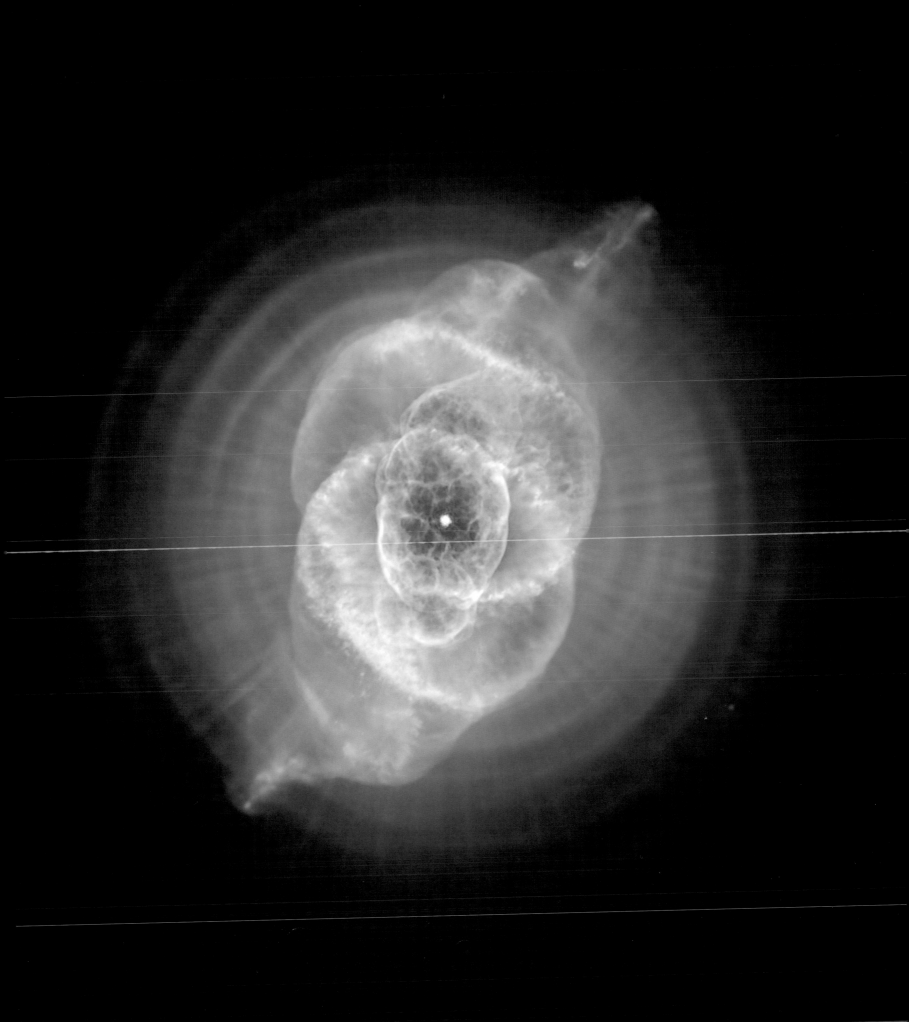

EAGLE NEBULA

The famous star-forming region of Messier 16 in the constellation of Serpens is painted with delicate pastel colours in this stunning wide-field image from Arizona's Kitt Peak National Observatory. The bright star cluster at the heart of the nebula discovered around 1745 by French astronomer Jean-Philippe Loys de Chéseaux, while Charles Messier first noted the surrounding nebula in 1764. It was only in the photographic age, however, that astronomers came to notice the nebula's resemblance to an eagle with outstretched wings, and it acquired its popular name.

In this false-colour image, hydrogen emission is shown in green, oxygen in blue and sulphur in red. The colour differences highlight the nebula's true structure – the outstretched 'wings' of the Eagle (spread diagonally across the image) in fact mark the interior of a huge star-forming cavern, lit by glowing gases within and hemmed in by dark surrounding dust clouds.

The entire nebula lies around 6,500 light years from Earth and the interior of the central cavern is perhaps 30 light years across. Within it, dark tendrils mark the sites where new stars are being formed – just to the right of centre lie the famous 'Pillars of Creation' photographed by the Hubble Space Telescope in 1995, while the elegant tower known as the Spire (see page 108) rises vertically at lower left of centre.

OBJECT **Eagle Nebula, M16**

DISTANCE **6,500 light years**

RA **18h 18m 51s**

DEC **-13° 49' 51"**

OBSERVED WITH **Kitt Peak National Observatory**

NSF 0.9-m Telescope

CENTAURUS A

Twin jets of matter erupting like fountains into intergalactic space form the focus in this multi-wavelength image of galaxy NGC 5128. This unusual galaxy in the southern constellation of Centaurus is perhaps better known by the designation of the powerful radio source at its centre, Centaurus A.

The composite combines a visible-light image from the European Southern Observatory's 2.2-metre (88-in) telescope at La Silla, with radio data (shown in orange) from ESO's APEX radio telescope and an X-ray image (in blue) from NASA's Chandra X-Ray Observatory. The visible galaxy is a ball of light bisected by a thick dust lane, the surviving remnant of a smaller spiral galaxy recently cannibalized by the larger one (see page 110). Narrow jets of high-speed, X-ray-emitting matter emerge from either side of the core, before billowing out into the lobes, which produce both X-ray and radio emission.

Centaurus A is one of the nearest examples of an active galaxy – one that contains an 'Active Galactic Nucleus' generating large quantities of radiation at its core. Active galaxies frequently display rapid variations in their output, or far more luminous cores than can be explained by stars alone – astronomers believe that their activity is generated when a supermassive black hole at the centre of the galaxy is 'fed' with large quantities of matter, often as a result of a galactic collision.

OBJECT **Centaurus A, NGC 5128**

DISTANCE **11 million light years**

RA **13h 25m 28s**

DEC **-43° 01' 09"**

OBSERVED WITH **European Southern Observatory**
MPG/ESO 2.2-m Telescope, Atacama Pathfinder
Experiment, Chandra X-Ray Observatory

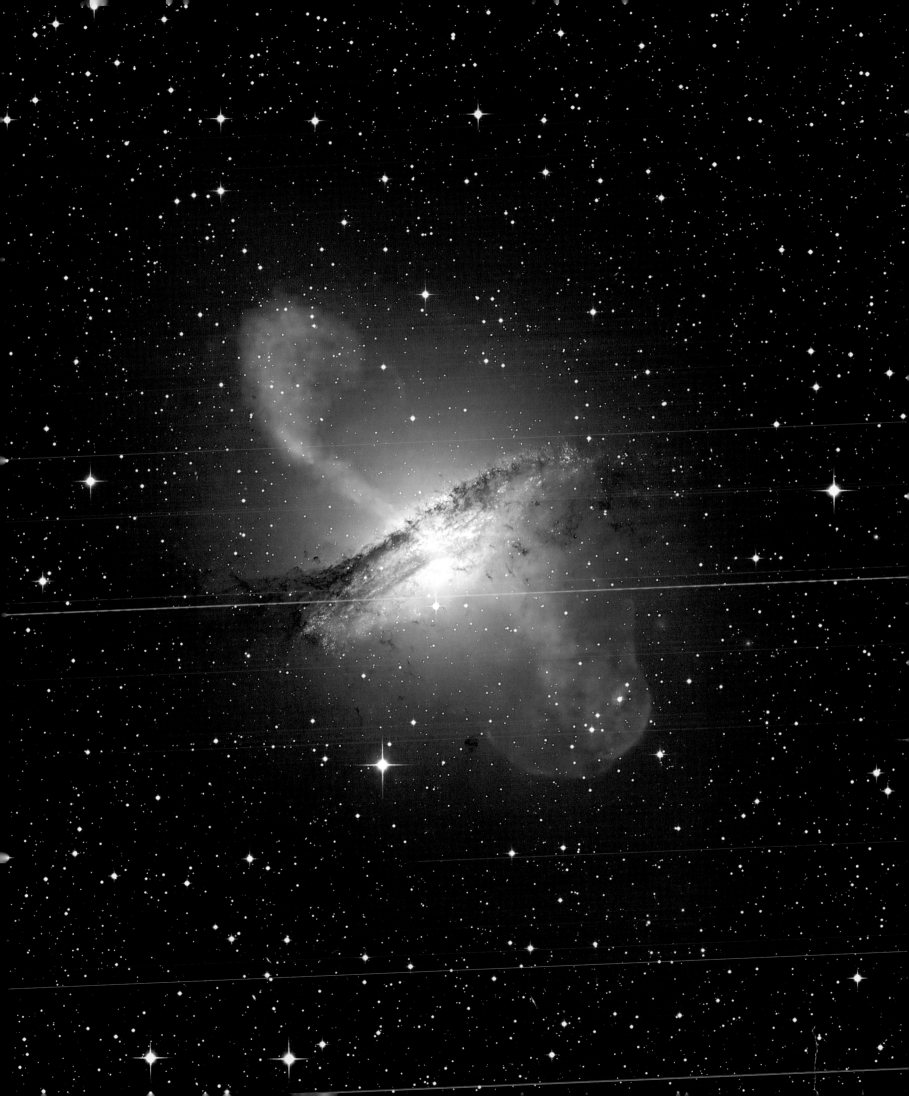

JUPITER FROM BELOW

Jupiter's southern hemisphere is rendered into a mass of concentric cloud patterns in this unusual view, constructed from data gathered with the Cassini spaceprobe during its December 2000 fly-by of the giant planet. This 'polar stereographic projection' stitches together data from 36 separate exposures taken over the course of nine hours as the spaceprobe passed by some 10 million kilometres (6.2 million miles) away.

Despite an equatorial diameter 11 times larger than Earth's, Jupiter rotates in just 9 hours and 56 minutes. This rapid rotation generates enormous influence over Jupiter's weather systems, wrapping high- and low-pressure systems into parallel bands around the equator to form the planet's distinctive creamy zones and reddish belts respectively. A ring of white-spot storms circles the planet at high southern latitudes, while other storms risk their survival through their proximity to the Great Red Spot. The large cream spot at the four o'clock position is Oval BA, which has since deepened and turned red, and is now commonly nicknamed 'Red Spot Junior'.

OBJECT **Jupiter**

MIN DISTANCE **629 million km**

(391 million miles)

DIAMETER **142,984 km (88,846 miles)**

OBSERVED WITH **Cassini Imaging Science Subsystem**

CAULDRON OF
STARBIRTH

This eerie image from NASA's Spitzer Space Telescope uses infrared light to peer through the dense Milky Way starfields and dark dust clouds in the northern constellation of Cygnus, revealing a seething mass of star-forming gas and dust.

This enormous complex, known as Cygnus X and originally identified through its radio emissions, is one of the richest starbirth regions in our galaxy, containing as many as 800 separate glowing nebulae and several clusters of newborn heavyweight stars – a special type of open cluster known as an 'OB association'. Light from these stars ionizes the surrounding gas for light years around, but all this activity is normally hidden from view – Cygnus X is 4,500 light years away, on the far side of our galaxy's Cygnus spiral arm and beyond a large cloud of interstellar dust, the Cygnus Rift, that lies just 300 light years from Earth.

This Spitzer view looks through all this intervening matter to map the temperatures within Cygnus X: red indicates the coolest temperatures, with green and blue marking warmer regions. The combination of colours means that active star-forming regions show up in yellow and white, while newborn stars appear blue. Some of the most prominent features within the nebula are bubbles, similar to the Bubble Nebula (see page 118), hollowed out of the gas by powerful stellar winds of heavyweight stars.

OBJECT **Cygnus X**

DISTANCE **4,500 light years**

RA **20h 32m 00s**

DEC **+40° 30' 00"**

OBSERVED WITH **Spitzer Space Telescope**

FROZEN BOOMERANG

The rainbow hues in this spectacular image recall the refracted colours of sunlight reflecting in a puddle of oil, but their origin is rather different. This composite view of the Boomerang Nebula in the southern constellation of Centaurus uses colour coding to distinguish between a series of polarized views. Each colour represents the light collected through a polarizing filter (similar to polaroid sunglass lenses) tuned to transmit light at a particular angle. The polarization of light at different angles is caused by light scattering off small dust particles in the nebula, and astronomers can use images such as this to study the distribution and size of these particles.

The Boomerang is a remarkable 'protoplanetary' nebula – a star with roughly the mass of our Sun that has reached the end of its red giant phase of evolution and is now rapidly shedding its outer layers. As the central star shrinks and heats up, its radiation will eventually cause the surrounding gas to fluoresce and form a true planetary nebula (see pages 20 and 180), but for the moment, the nebula shines largely through reflection of starlight.

Lying around 5,000 light years from Earth, the nebula is about two light years across, and gas within it is expanding at speeds of more than 160 kilometres per second (100 miles per second). The rapid expansion cools the nebula to extreme temperatures of -272°C (-458°F), just 1°C (1.8°F) above absolute zero. This makes the Boomerang the coldest place in the Universe.

OBJECT **Boomerang Nebula, M16**

DISTANCE **5,000 light years**

RA **12h 44m 46s**

DEC **-54° 31' 12"**

OBSERVED WITH **Hubble Space Telescope**

Advanced Camera for Surveys

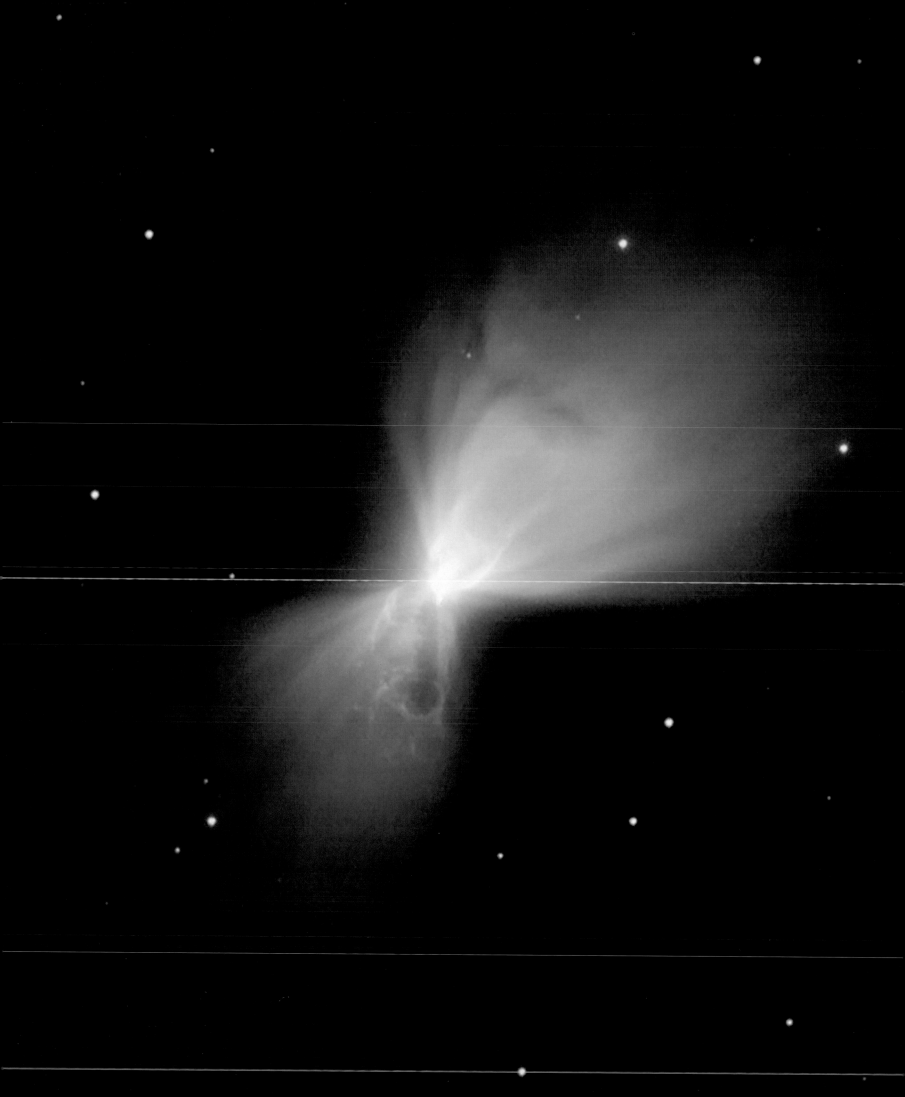

POCKET OF STARBIRTH

A shockwave created as intense stellar winds blow across this star-forming region creates a sharp 'wall' at the centre of this nebula, in which some astronomers see the profile of a human face. NGC 3324 lies about 7,500 light years from Earth in the southern constellation of Carina, and is closely associated with the better known and brighter Carina Nebula that lies nearby. It shows the aftermath of starbirth – a wave of compression passed through this region a few million years ago, triggering the creation of the bright stars that now dominate this image. Radiation from these stars now illuminates the nebula from within through excitation of its atoms. The crimson glow spread across the image is generated by hydrogen atoms, while the yellow-white light inside of the cavity emanates from oxygen.

Close-up images of the central wall from the Hubble Space Telescope reveal detail only suggested in this wide-field image. Towering pillars of gas stand out where they are dense enough to resist the erosion of the stellar winds, and compression triggered by the passing shockwave may ultimately give rise to another generation of stars.

OBJECT **NGC 3324**

DISTANCE **7,500 light years**

RA **10h 37m 20s**

DEC **-58° 31' 30"**

OBSERVED WITH

European Southern Observatory

MPG/ESO 2.2-m Telescope

➤ OPPOSITE

SATURN'S HALO

The intricate ring system around Saturn comes to spectacular life when illuminated from behind in this astonishing image from the Cassini spaceprobe. This view combines 165 separate images at infrared, visible and ultraviolet wavelengths, collected over a period of nine hours as Cassini sped over Saturn's night side. The resulting composite exaggerates variations in colour and brightness in order to reveal differences in the properties of the ring particles.

The Cassini mosaic captures the main rings in unprecedented detail. From the cloudtops of Saturn outwards, they are: the near-invisible D ring, the semi-transparent C or 'Crepe' ring, the bright B and A rings, the thread-like F ring (running around the outer edge of the A ring), the much paler G ring and the broad expanse of the E ring around the orbit of the icy moon Enceladus (see page 178). This wonderful image also contains an unexpected bonus – the pale blue dot just inside the G ring at the ten o'clock position is our own planet, Earth.

OBJECT **Saturn**

MIN DISTANCE **1.2 billion km**

(750 million miles)

DIAMETER **120,536 km (74,898 miles)**

OBSERVED WITH **Cassini**

Imaging Science Subsystem

➤➤ OVERLEAF

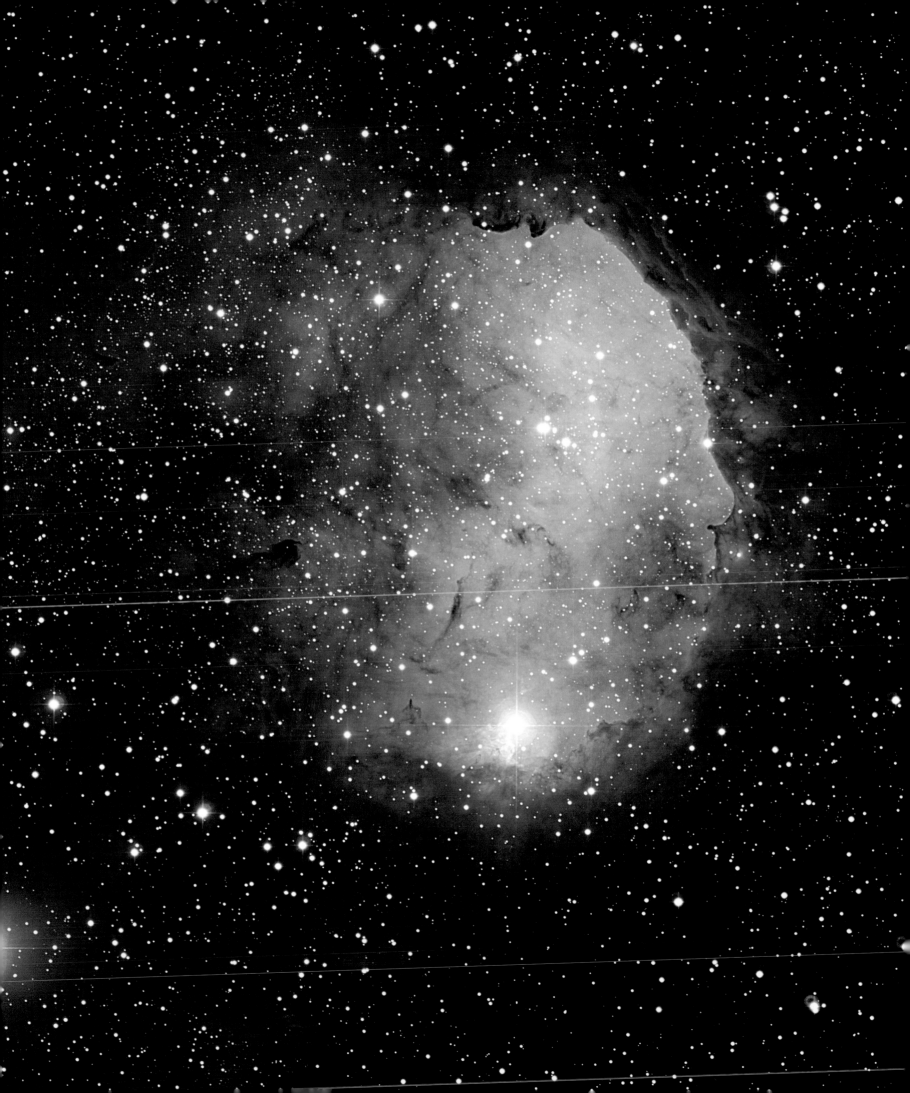

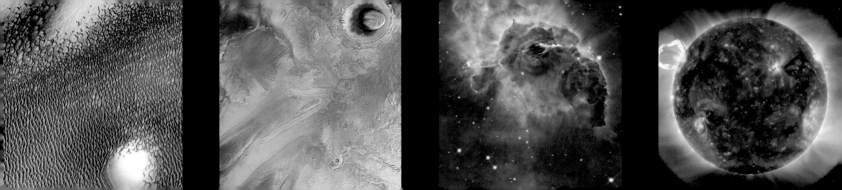

FIRE AND ICE 5

RINGS OF URANUS

A section across the narrow ring system of Uranus, the seventh planet from the Sun, resembles a multicoloured barcode in this computer-enhanced image from the Voyager 2 spaceprobe. Nine rings are visible here, fringed by broad pastel lines that arise from the imaging process. Six separate images, at three different wavelengths were combined in order to accurately detect colour differences between the rings – the final false-colour view boosts the colours considerably in order to make these differences clearer, producing a beautiful multi-banded image in the process.

The rings around Uranus were discovered in 1977, when astronomers waiting to record the planet's passage in front of a star noticed a series of dips in the star's light before and after the 'occultation' event itself. A total of 13 rings are now known, each very thin, dark and sharply defined in comparison to the broad planes encircling Saturn. Thanks to Uranus's extreme tilt – its poles are lined up almost in the plane of its orbit – the rings give Uranus a 'bullseye' appearance when seen from Earth.

The outermost and brightest ring is the Epsilon Ring, at extreme right in this image. The others are far fainter, narrower and darker, and there are distinct colour differences between the creamy-white of Epsilon and the blue-green of the inner rings. In contrast to the bright rings of Saturn, which are dominated by water ice, the Uranian system clearly contains large amounts of darker material, such as dust or frozen methane.

OBJECT **Uranus**

MIN DISTANCE **2.6 billion km (1.5 billion miles)**

DIAMETER **51,118 km (31,763 miles)**

OBSERVED WITH **Voyager 2 Imaging Science Subsystem**

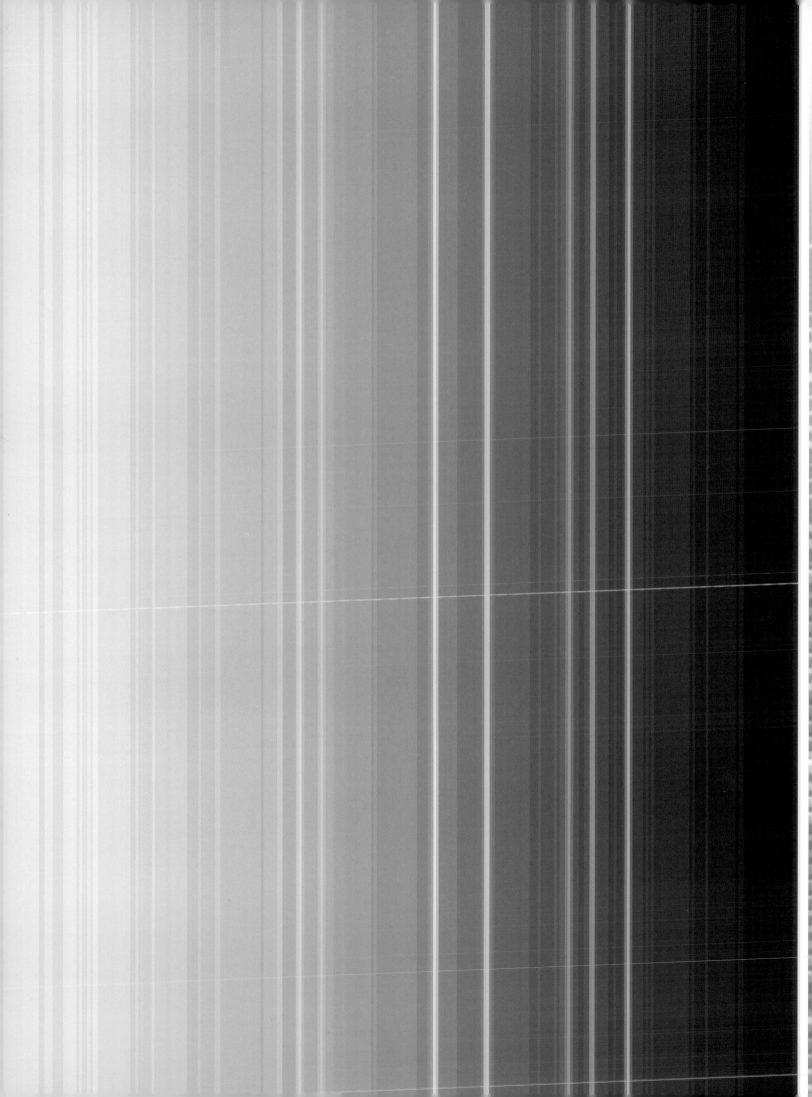

DIAMOND RING

One last sliver of sunlight blazes out from behind the Moon's dark disc in the moments before a solar eclipse becomes total. Known as the diamond ring effect, this, along with the related 'Baily's beads', is one of the most celebrated eclipse phenomena. Beads are created as chinks of sunlight shine through valleys around the Moon's edge during the 'totality' itself, and the diamond ring effect is seen when just one bead remains.

For astronomers, eclipses are not just beautiful and eerie events – they also offer a rare chance to study the Sun's sparse outer atmosphere or corona. This was especially true before the dawn of the Space Age, when it became possible for satellites to create artificial eclipses simply by placing an 'occulting disc' across the Sun's bright face.

The brilliant solar disc, known as the photosphere, marks the boundary at which the Sun's gases become transparent and sunlight can finally stream away into space. It has a depth of around 500 kilometres (300 miles) and defines a sphere roughly 1.4 million kilometres (870,000 miles) across. However, the Sun's outer layers actually extend far beyond this. Directly above the photosphere lies a thin layer called the chromosphere in which much of the Sun's activity occurs. Beyond this lie the transition zone and the corona, a region in which the gas is tenuous but extremely hot – while temperatures in the photosphere are a 'mere' 5,500°C (9,900°F), those in the corona reach more than 1 million°C (1.8 million°F).

OBJECT **The Sun**

MEAN DISTANCE **149.6 million km (93 million miles)**

DIAMETER **1.392 million km (865,000 miles)**

OBSERVED WITH **Amateur equipment**

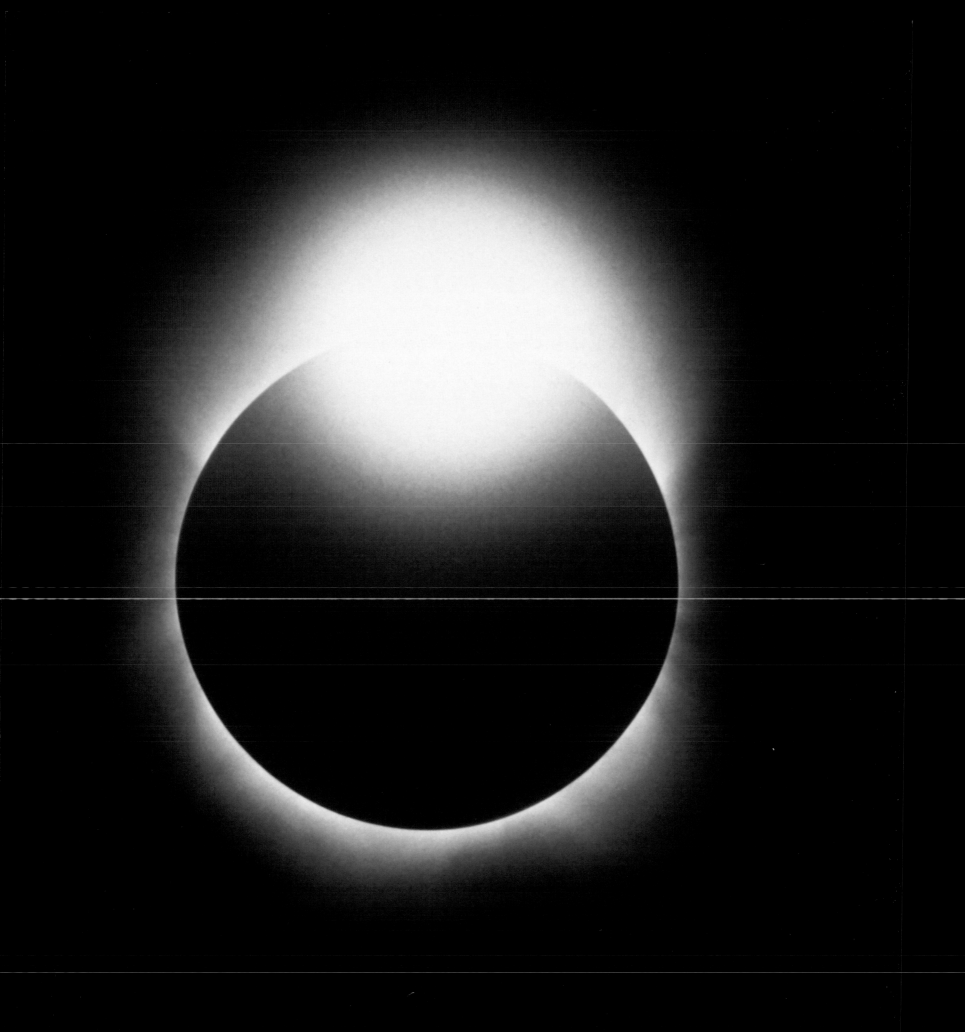

JETS IN CARINA

A glowing outcrop of star-forming gas and dust looms like an ominous thunderhead in the Carina Nebula, NGC 3372, some 7,500 light years from Earth. As the tip of this 'pillar of creation', some three light years long, is heated and sculpted by radiation from unseen stars above, gases boil away into space, generating a halo of luminous rays.

Within the roiling clouds of gas and dust that form the bulk of this pillar, new stars are forming. The process of starbirth begins when a relatively small region of the nebula begins to collapse under its own gravity, flattening into a bulging disc that begins to spin more rapidly. At the centre of this disc, an infant protostar begins to form, drawing in more material and heating up as it grows denser. Excess material that is not drawn into the star itself tends to be flung off in opposite directions along the axis of the spinning disc, creating a structure called a 'bipolar outflow', exemplified by jets of gas visible to either side of the dark blob near the top of the pillar. Gas in these jets is thought to be moving at around 1.4 million kilometres per hour (850,000 mph), and the entire jet (which can be traced through glowing knots where it collides with the surrounding gas clouds) has an estimated length of ten light years.

OBJECT **Carina Nebula, NGC 3372**

DISTANCE **7,500 light years**

RA **10h 43m 52s**

DEC **-59° 55' 21"**

OBSERVED WITH **Hubble Space Telescope**

Wide Field Camera 3

TRITON

Neptune's largest satellite presents a unique blend of pale greens and browns, illuminated by the feeble light of a distant Sun, in this image captured by the Voyager 2 spaceprobe. This strange moon is one of the coldest worlds in the solar system, with a surface temperature of around -235°C (-391°F), but is surprisingly active. The smoother pale brown regions of its southern hemisphere are painted with streaks of dust marking the paths of 'ice geysers' – jets of vaporized material rising high into Triton's sparse atmosphere. Astronomers believe that Triton owes its activity to heating from tidal forces, rather like the active moons of Jupiter and Saturn. In this case, though, the tides have an unusual cause. Triton is thought to be a rogue world, captured into orbit around Neptune at some point in its history and gradually slowed by strong tides that forced it into its present-day orbit, perfectly circular but the 'wrong way' around Neptune. At its peak, the tidal heating melted large chunks of the moon's crust, resulting in the lumpy green-blue 'cantaloupe terrain' around Triton's equator.

During its 1989 fly-by of the most distant planet, Voyager 2 was travelling at roughly three times the speed of the Apollo lunar spacecraft, while the objects being photographed were so faint that exposures of a minute or more were required to capture their light. Fortunately, the spaceprobe was equipped with a movable camera platform that adjusted as Voyager tracked along its flight path to keep Triton directly in view.

OBJECT **Triton**

SATELLITE OF **Neptune**

MIN DISTANCE **4.3 billion km (2.7 billion miles)**

DIAMETER **2,707 km (1,682 miles)**

OBSERVED WITH **Voyager 2 Imaging Science Subsystem**

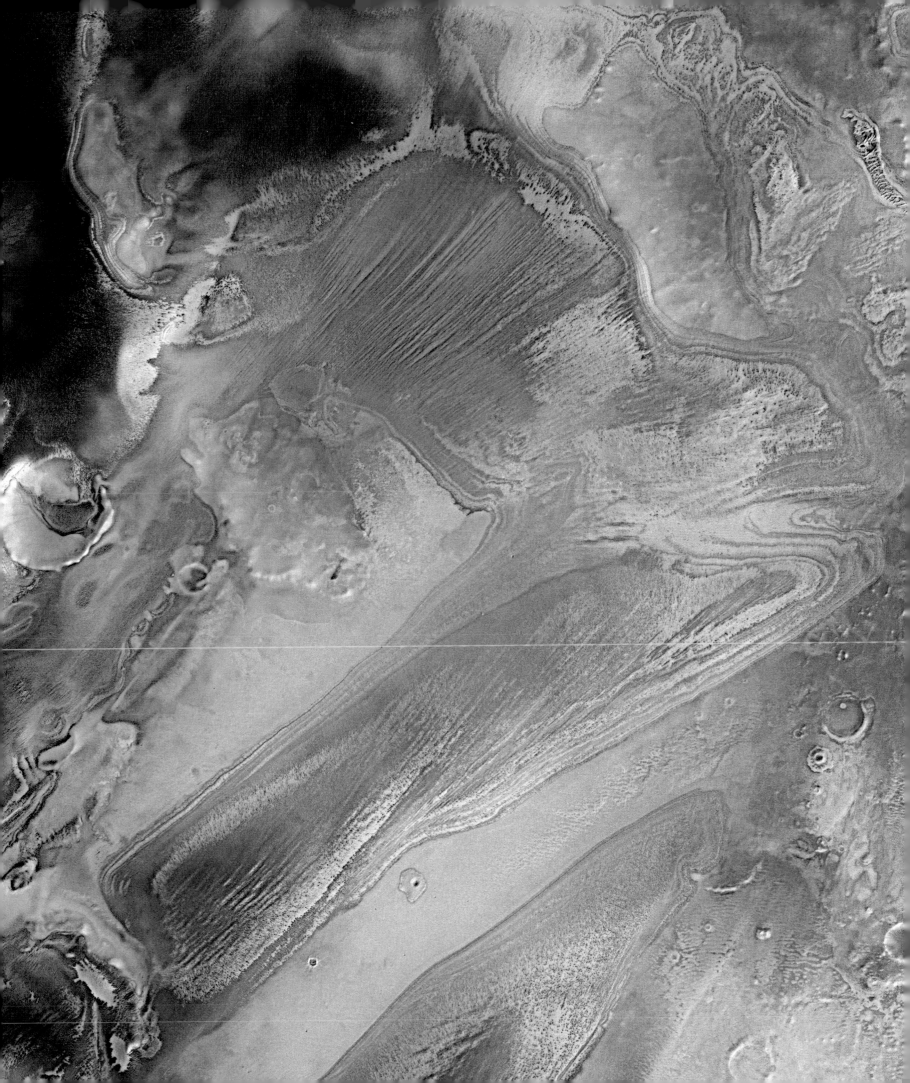

THE SUPERHOT SUN

This bizarre view of our local star transforms the surface from its usual blazing, near-featureless disc to a seething ball of multilayered gas clouds. The image depicts the Sun in extreme ultraviolet wavelengths, as seen by the Atmospheric Imaging Assembly instrument on board NASA's Solar Dynamics Observatory. These wavelengths of radiation are generated by gas at temperatures ranging from 5,000°C (9,000°F) up to 2 million°C (3.6 million°F) or more. False colours correspond to gas at different temperatures, with reds a relatively cool 60,000°C (108,000°F) and blues and greens much hotter, at 1 million°C (1.8 million°F) plus.

Surrounding the central disc are pinkish loops and streaks known as prominences – outbursts of relatively cool, dense gas emerging from the photosphere along magnetic field lines. A much brighter, hotter and more intense prominence arcs high above the Sun at the ten o'clock position, tracing a large loop of solar magnetic field. Beyond these features, the superhot (but tenuous) gases of the Sun's outer atmosphere, or corona, stream away from all sides.

Images such as this one reveal that the Sun's magnetic field is constantly changing and evolving in an 11-year cycle that sees it rise and fall in intensity as the centres of magnetic activity move from high latitudes towards the equator. The position and strength of the field affects the frequency and intensity of prominences, solar flares and dark sunspots on the Sun's visible surface.

OBJECT **The Sun**

MEAN DISTANCE **149.6 million km (93 million miles)**

DIAMETER: **1.392 million km (865,000 miles)**

OBSERVED WITH **Solar Dynamics Observatory**

Atmospheric Imaging Assembly

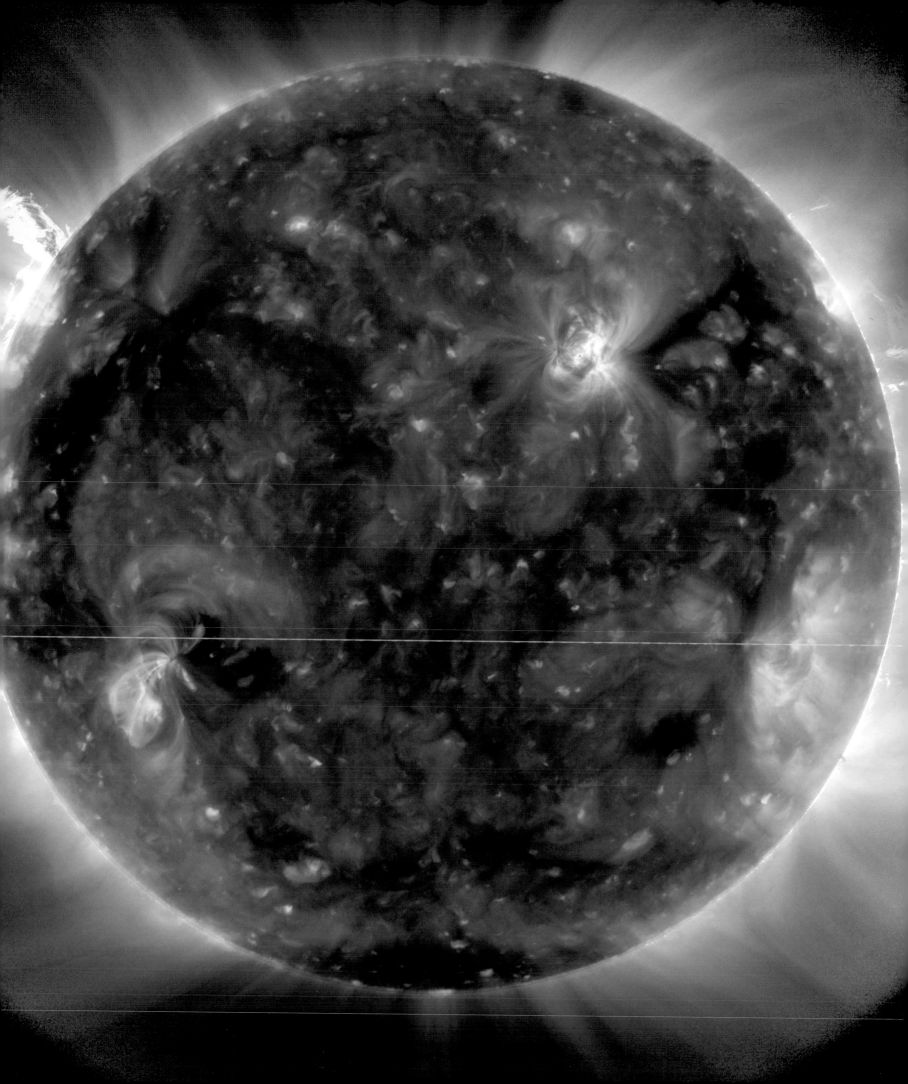

MARTIAN ICE CAP

A computer-generated map of the region around the Martian south pole creates a startling multicoloured abstract in this image, produced by combined data from the European Space Agency's Mars Express and NASA's Mars Global Surveyor. Colours in the map depict the thickness of ice-rich 'layered deposits' that build up in the Martian antarctic. These layers are almost entirely composed of water ice with a little of the planet's characteristic red dust mixed in, and range in depth from just a few metres or tens of metres at their fringes (see page 160), up to more than 3.7 kilometres (2.3 miles) at the south pole itself. Colours ranging from purple to red indicate the increasing thickness of ice, while the exposed south polar ice cap is outlined in black. The central circle marks the area poleward of 87 degrees south, beyond the range of Mars Express instruments.

The map was constructed using the Mars Express MARSIS radar instrument, a penetrating radar whose signals can pass straight through the ice to reflect off the ground at its base. By measuring the time for signals to bounce back from the top and base of the ice, its thickness can be calculated, and this can then be combined with a high-resolution map of surface relief from Mars Global Surveyor. The total volume of ice within these deposits is enough to form a layer 11 metres (36 ft) deep if spread evenly across the Martian surface.

OBJECT **Mars**

MIN DISTANCE **54.6 million km (33.9 million miles)**

DIAMETER **6,792 km (4,220 miles)**

OBSERVED WITH

Mars Global Surveyor Mars Orbiter Laser Altimeter,

Mars Express MARSIS Radar

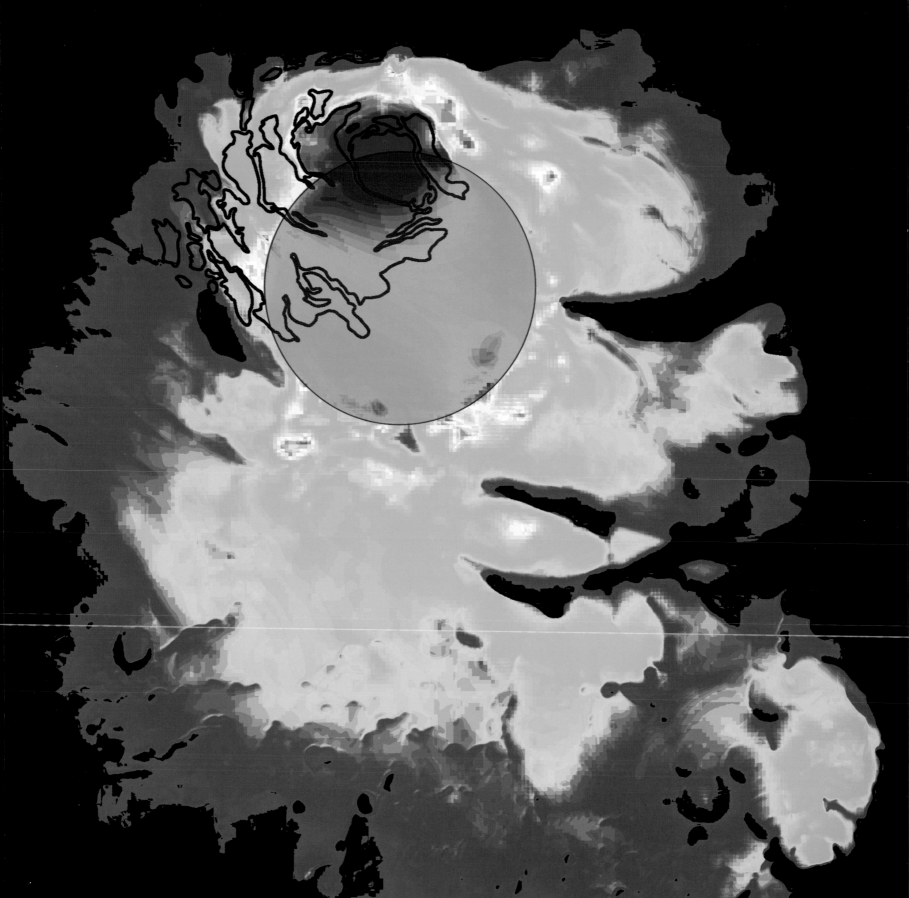

HYPERION

Resembling nothing so much as a curious bath sponge as it floats in the darkness of space, Saturn's satellite Hyperion has a good claim to be the strangest moon in the solar system. At first glance, the heavy pitting across its surface looks like the impact cratering typical on many other worlds, but closer inspection reveals something far more unusual – a spongy structure consisting of dark pits separated by razor-sharp ridges of brighter material. This strange appearance is probably the result of weak sunlight slowly eroding the moon's original cratered surface – evaporating the icy element of Hyperion's rock/ice mix so that dark, dusty material crumbles inwards while the remaining bright material is fashioned into serrated peaks. One result of this process is that Hyperion is now highly porous, with up to half of its interior made up of empty space.

But Hyperion's curiosities do not end there – orbiting Saturn some way beyond the giant satellite Titan, it circles the ringed planet in 21 days and 6 hours, but spins chaotically, with no set rotation period, or even axis of rotation. With a long axis of 360 kilometres (225 miles) it is also rather too big to be as misshapen as it is – Hyperion's gravity should have pulled it into a more spherical shape during its formation. The likely explanation is that Hyperion represents the surviving core of a moon that was once much larger, but was mostly destroyed in a long-lost cosmic collision.

OBJECT **Hyperion**

SATELLITE OF **Saturn**

MIN DISTANCE **1.2 billion km (750 million miles)**

DIAMETER **5,152 km (3,201 miles)**

OBSERVED WITH **Cassini Imaging Science Subsystem**

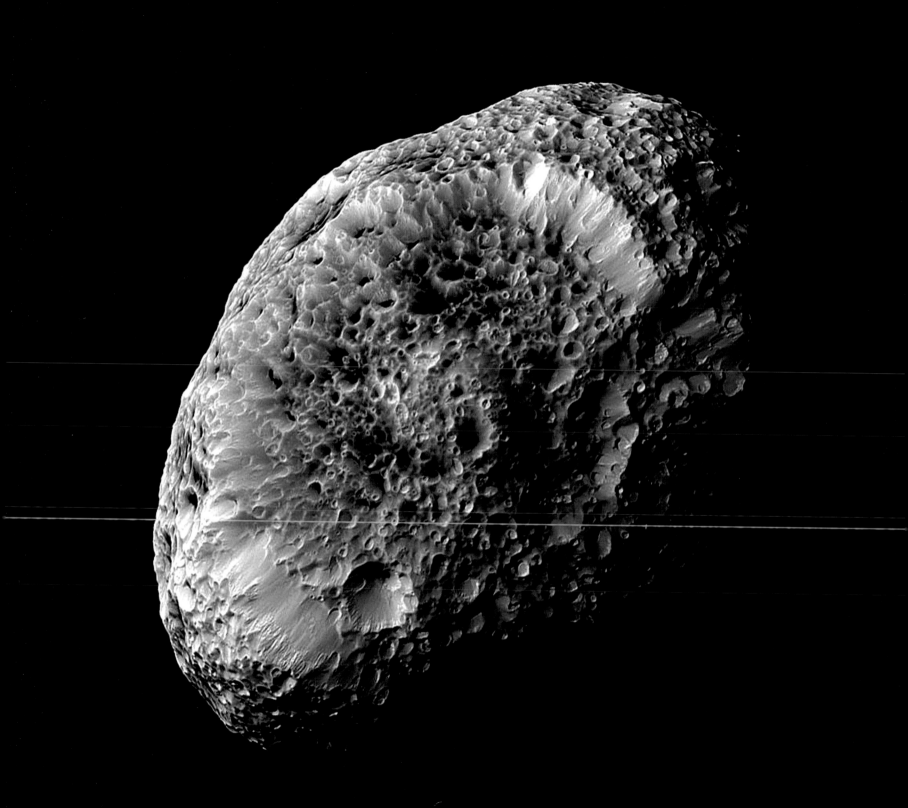

THARSIS THOLUS

The startling colours of this elevation map reveal the secrets of an extinct Martian volcano, uncovering an unseen history of eruption and later collapse. With a peak rising to 8 kilometres (5 miles) above the surrounding terrain, Tharsis Tholus is a volcano on the scale of Earth's Mount Everest, but by Martian standards is little more than average. The base of the volcano covers roughly 155 x 125 kilometres (95 x 78 miles), while its sunken central caldera is roughly 33 kilometres (20 miles) in diameter. Steep cliffs around the caldera plunge by up to 2,700 metres (8,850 ft), while two other sharply delineated escarpments trace further collapses.

Tharsis, like all large Martian volcanoes, is a volcanic shield. A multilayered mass of lava has built up through sustained eruptions as lava has poured onto the surface through fissures along its flanks, fed by an underground reservoir of molten magma. The oldest parts of the volcano seem to have formed around 4 billion years ago, but at some point the magma reservoir drained away, causing the shield to subside and form the caldera and other escarpments in separate collapse events. While volcanoes are widespread across the Martian surface, most of the large shields, including Olympus Mons – the largest volcano in the solar system – are concentrated in a region known as the Tharsis Rise. This enormous bulge in the Martian surface rises up to 8 kilometres (5 miles) above the average Martian ground level, and is thought to mark the location of an ancient 'hot spot' in the planet's interior.

OBJECT **Mars**

MIN DISTANCE **54.6 million km (33.9 million miles)**

DIAMETER **6,792 km (4,220 miles)**

OBSERVED WITH **Mars Express**

High-Resolution Stereo Camera

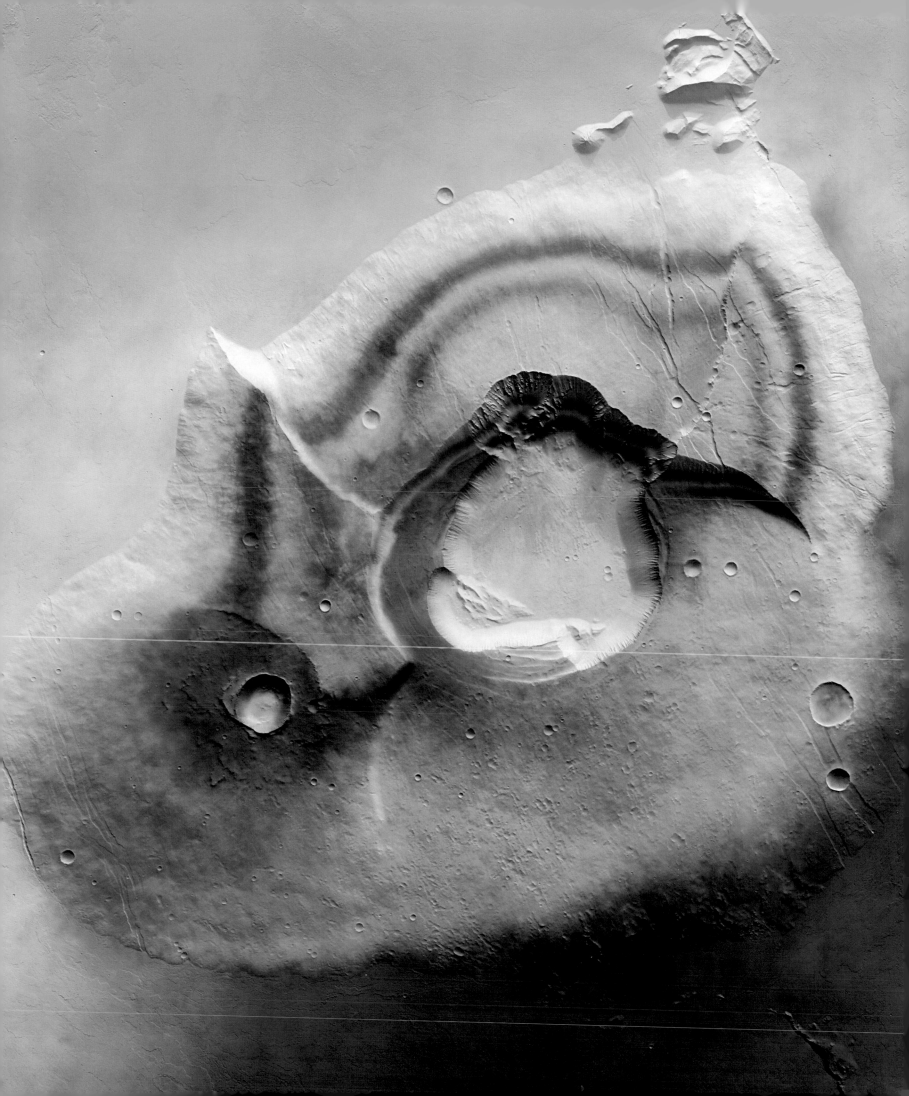

SUNSPOTS

This writhing mass of cells and tendrils is more reminiscent of a microscope slide than the surface of our Sun. But in fact it is a view of the Sun's visible photosphere, imaged at one narrow wavelength in order to block most of the light and reveal unseen detail. This picture, taken by the Swedish Solar Telescope on La Palma, shows the curious landscape created by hot gas and magnetic fields around a large sunspot group.

Sunspots are the most obvious solar features visible from Earth – dark patches on the Sun's bright disc with lifespans that typically range between days and weeks, and which are carried across the Sun's face by its rotation in periods of 25–30 days depending on their latitude. The spots appear dark only because they are cool in comparison to their surroundings – at around 3,500°C (6,300°F), they are around 2,000°C (3,600°F) cooler than the average photospheric temperature. Growing up to tens of thousands of kilometres across, they form as loops in the solar magnetic field force their way out through the photosphere into the upper atmosphere, creating a cooler region of lower density at their exit and re-entry points. Arcs of gas called prominences loop through the Sun's outer atmosphere between spots.

Surrounding the spots in this image are other features of the solar surface – long, rising pillars of flame called 'spicules', and networks of dark-edged, bright-centred, cell-like structures known as granulation. Individual cells may be thousand of kilometres wide, and each marks the top of a rising column of hot gas from within the Sun.

OBJECT **The Sun**

MEAN DISTANCE **149.6 million km (93 million miles)**

DIAMETER: **1.392 million km (865,000 miles)**

OBSERVED WITH **Swedish Solar Telescope, La Palma**

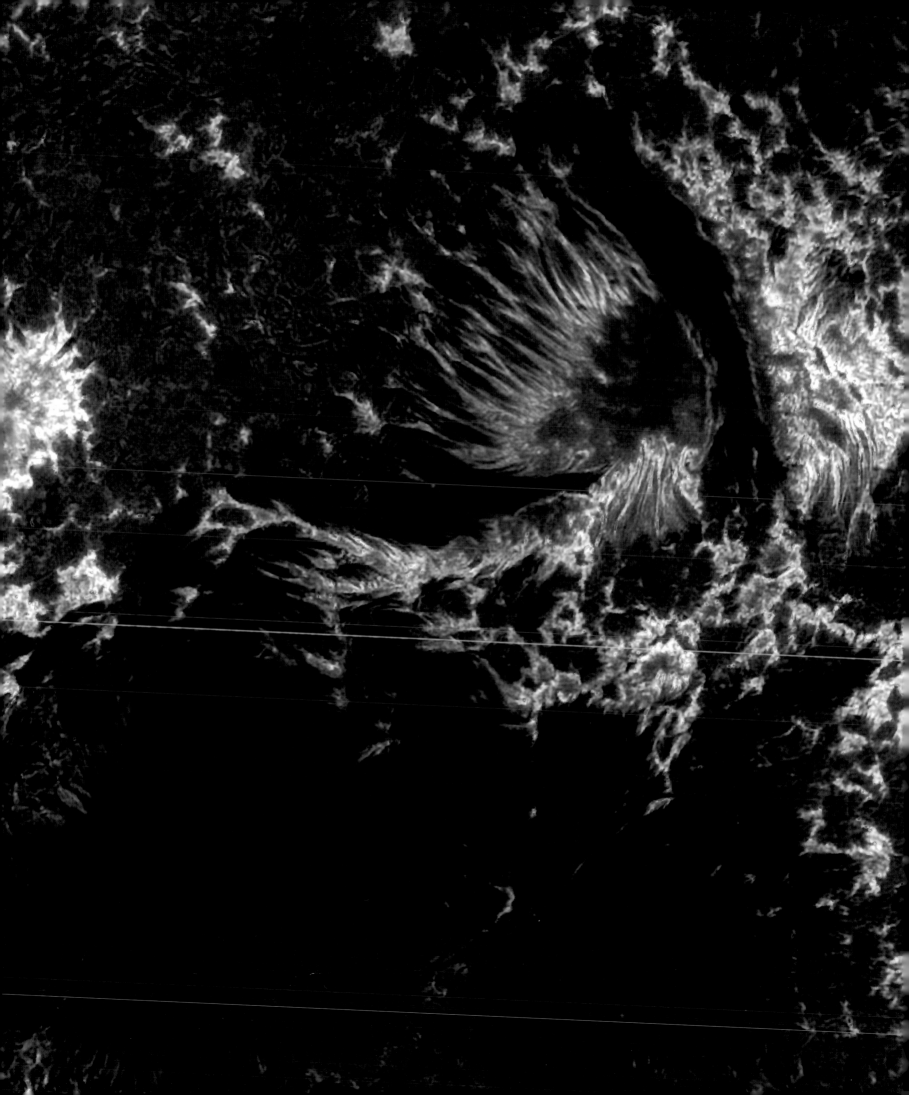

POLAR DUNEFIELD

Contrasting colours reveal varying temperatures across the Martian dune sea at high latitudes, in this false-colour image from NASA's Mars Odyssey orbiter. This spacecraft, which arrived in orbit around the Red Planet in October 2001, was equipped with an array of sensors to monitor the properties of the Martian atmosphere and surface, such as temperature and chemical composition. The scene combines images taken between December 2002 and November 2004 using Odyssey's THEMIS (Thermal Emission Imaging System) instrument, and reveals warmer areas in yellow and orange, cooler areas in blue and white. The darker sands within the dunes absorb more heat than the underlying soil and therefore appear warmer in this image.

This image covers a region roughly 30 kilometres (19 miles) across at a latitude of 80 degrees north and shows how dunes around the Martian poles are sculpted by prevailing winds into elongated crescents. While the south polar region in particular is rich in subsurface water-ice layers, the visible polar ice caps are overlaid with carbon dioxide frosts that build up in each hemisphere's autumn and evaporate in the spring. This effectively transfers carbon dioxide from pole to pole and back throughout each year, and helps generate the prevailing winds that not only sculpt the dunes, but are also responsible for the swirling patterns seen within the polar ice caps themselves.

OBJECT **Mars**

MIN DISTANCE **54.6 million km (33.9 million miles)**

DIAMETER **6,792 km (4,220 miles)**

OBSERVED WITH **Mars Odyssey Thermal Emission Imaging System**

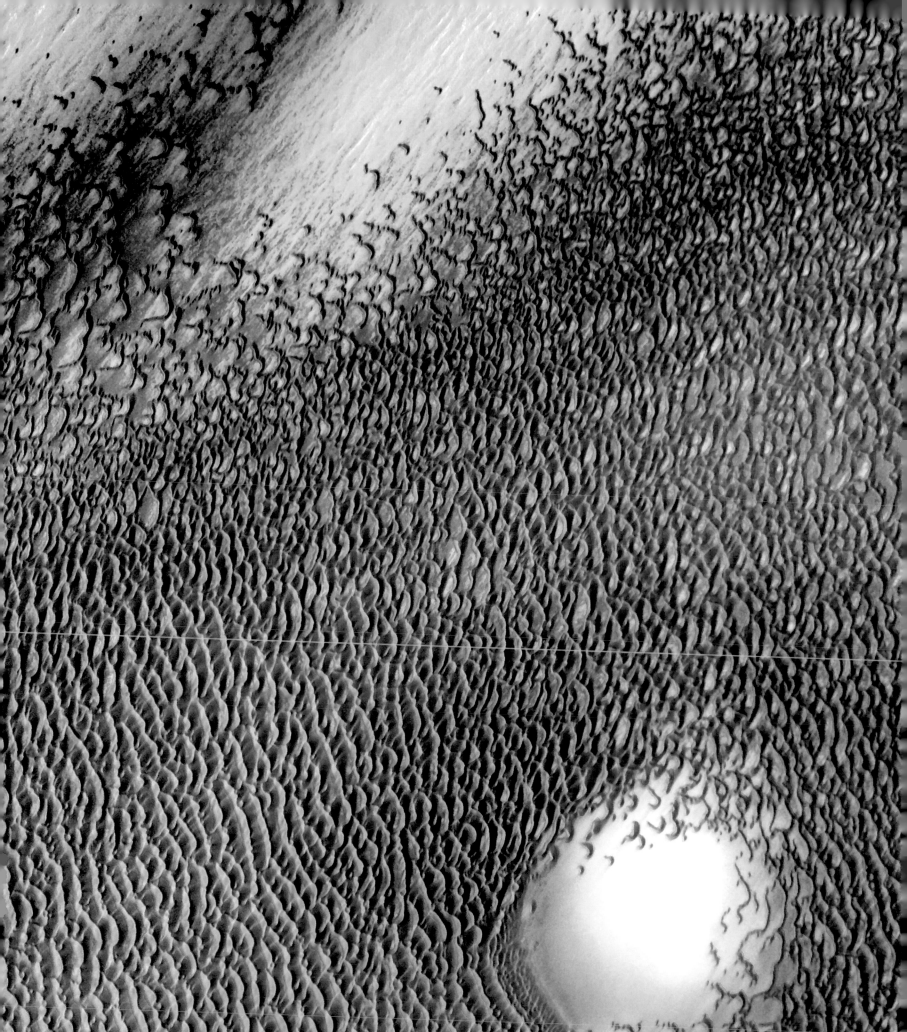

DESCENT OVER TITAN

The four horizontal strips in this extraordinary image chronicle a descent through the atmosphere of an alien world. Each is a panoramic mosaic captured by the European Space Agency's Huygens probe as it parachuted towards the surface of Titan on 14 January, 2005.

The opaque haze surrounding Titan had both frustrated and intrigued scientists ever since the Voyager fly-bys of the early 1980s, and the Cassini/Huygens mission represented a concerted effort to unravel its mysteries. Unlike its predecessors, Cassini was equipped with an infrared camera capable of seeing through Titan's atmosphere to reveal a surprisingly Earth-like pattern of features on the surface. Huygens, meanwhile, parachuted down near an equatorial region known as Xanadu, sending back images of a landscape unmistakably shaped by fluid erosion before finally touching down in what appeared to be a dried-up river estuary. Although planetary scientists had hoped that the probe might find liquid methane – either raining from the atmosphere or collecting in lakes on the surface – they were at first frustrated. However, the subsequent discovery of lakes near Titan's poles (see page 22) has since confirmed that Titan has a complex, methane-driven climate, and that Huygens may just have landed in a dry season.

OBJECT **Titan**

SATELLITE OF **Saturn**

MIN DISTANCE **1.2 billion km**
 (750 million miles)

DIAMETER **5,152 km (3,201 miles)**

OBSERVED WITH **Huygens Descent Imager/**
 Spectral Radiometer

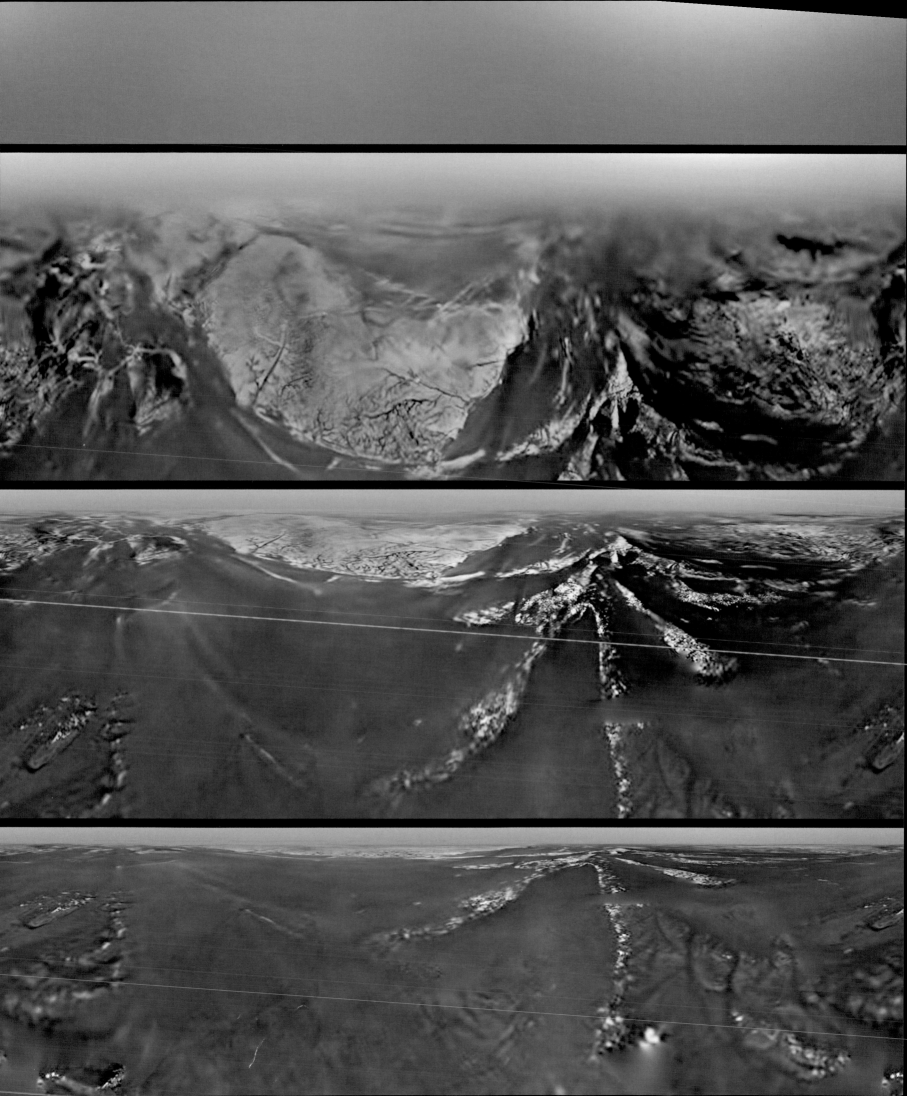

SNOWS OF ENCELADUS

Saturn's moon Enceladus presents a hemisphere of gleaming whites and blues in this pin-sharp enhanced-colour image from the Cassini spaceprobe. In normal light, the satellite appears brilliant white – the most reflective and therefore brightest landscape in the solar system – but here colour differences have been exaggerated to highlight features such as faults and the 'tiger stripes' of the southern hemisphere. Enceladus owes its pristine appearance to a widespread covering of fresh snow, produced by geyser eruptions from reservoirs of liquid water just below the surface. The existence of such geysers was just a hypothesis until Cassini flew through one shortly after its arrival in orbit around Saturn. Measurements showed that the crystallizing ice crystals were almost pure water.

As with several other satellites in the outer solar system, it's thought that Enceladus owes its activity to tidal heating – caused in this case by a gravitational tug-of-war between Saturn and the outer moon Dione. The tiger stripe features are thought to mark areas where the tidal stresses are greatest and the temperature of the icy crust is warmest, and most of the geyser eruptions can be traced to this region. While much of the water from these eruptions falls back as snow to blanket the surrounding terrain, substantial quantities escape the moon's gravity and fall into orbit around Saturn to form the planet's diaphanous 'E ring' (see page 146).

OBJECT **Enceladus**

SATELLITE OF **Saturn**

MIN DISTANCE **1.2 billion km (750 million miles)**

DIAMETER **504 km (313 miles)**

OBSERVED WITH **Cassini Imaging Science Subsystem**

COSMIC BUTTERFLY

Spreading its brightly coloured wings across the darkness of space, the Butterfly or Bug Nebula, NGC 6302, is a spectacular and dynamic celestial structure – far removed, it might seem, from the placid calm of objects such as the Ring and Helix Nebulae (see pages 20 and 116). Yet all of these objects are the same in essence – they are all planetary nebulae, created as a dying Sun-like star shrugs off its outer layers.

The main difference between these contrasting objects, in fact, is one of perspective. Seen from side-on, the Butterfly reveals that material is blowing out from the star in expanding bubbles, girdled around the middle by a dense ring of dust. The Ring and Helix, in contrast, lie end-on to Earth, so their appearance is dominated by the circular edge of the bubbles.

The central star of the Butterfly is hidden from view behind the doughnut-shaped dust ring, but its effects on the surrounding nebulosity reveal one of the hottest stars known, with an estimated surface temperature of 200,000°C (360,000°F). The dust ring itself, meanwhile, contains a variety of chemicals including carbon-based compounds, the mineral calcite and 'hailstones' of frozen water ice. These chemicals are thought to have formed in the upper atmosphere of the star as it passed through its cool red giant phase and have now been released into the surrounding nebula. The bright central pair of bubbles are thought to have been ejected around 2,000 years ago, but the faint ghosts of previous bubbles can be traced further out.

OBJECT **Butterfly Nebula, NGC 6302**

DISTANCE **3,800 light years**

RA **17h 13m 43s**

DEC **-37° 06' 10"**

OBSERVED WITH **Hubble Space Telescope Wide Field Camera 3**

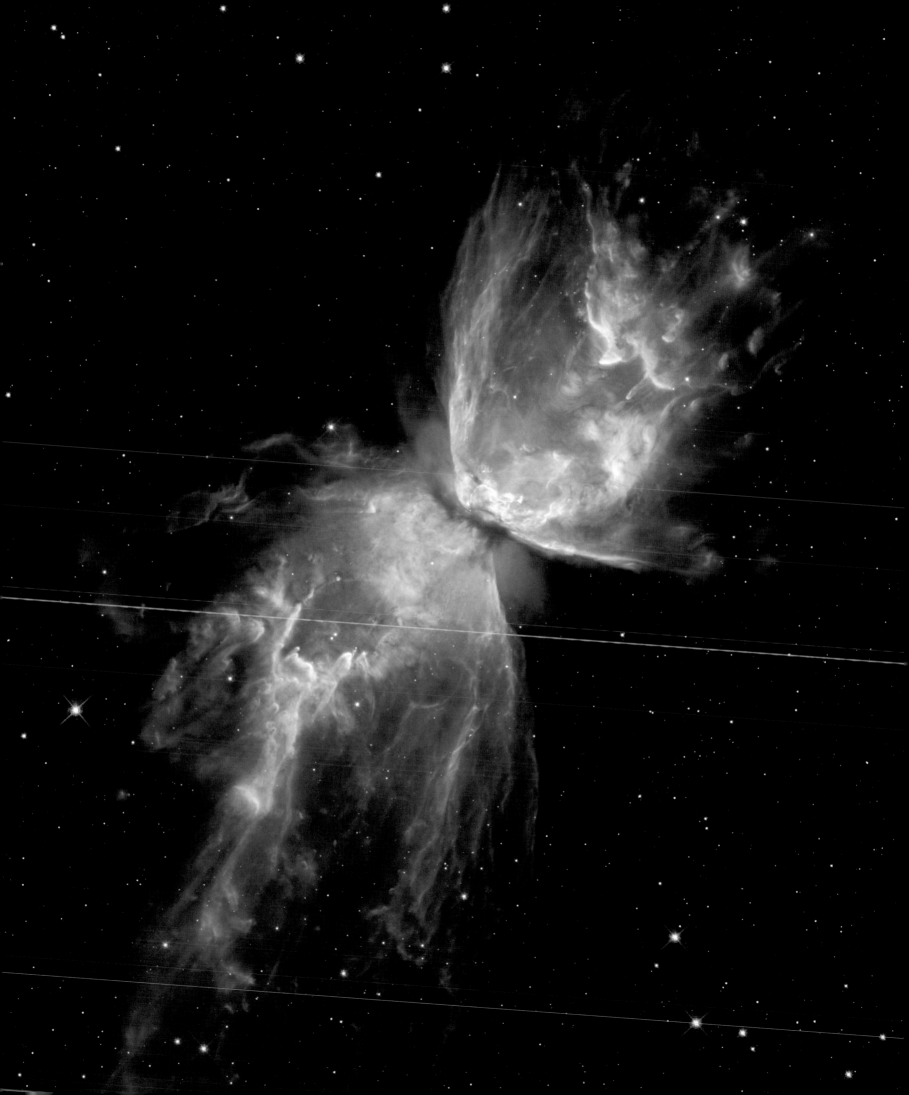

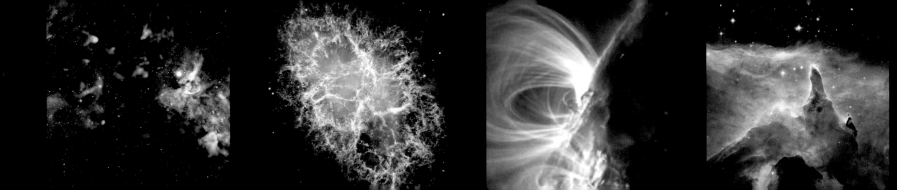

BEGINNINGS
AND ENDINGS

6

STARBIRTH IN THE
SOUTHERN CROWN

Ghostly clouds of light and dark swirl around one another in a maelstrom of star formation that blocks the light of more distant star clouds. This unusual nebulosity surrounds the stars R Coronae Australis (top) and TY Coronae Australis (below), roughly 420 light years from Earth. Both R and TY vary their brightness unpredictably – they are still shedding excess material and pulsating in size as they settle down towards their long stellar middle age.

These two young and relatively lightweight stars do not produce enough ultraviolet light to excite the gas around them and create the pinkish glow of an emission nebula – instead, they light up their surroundings through reflection alone. Scattering in the nebula tends to deflect short-wavelength blue light more than long-wavelength red light, and so the reflection nebula takes on a ghostly blue hue.

A dark finger of gas enters the picture from the left – part of the cloud of stellar raw materials that gave birth to both of these stars. New generations of young stars glow faintly from within this nebula, and are more easily detected using infrared instruments that can pierce the opaque dust. The entire region shown in this image from the European Southern Observatory's La Silla Observatory in Chile covers roughly the diameter of the Full Moon, corresponding to an area about four light years across.

OBJECT **R and TY Coronae Australis**

DISTANCE **420 light years**

RA **19h 01m 54s**

DEC **-36° 57' 08"**

OBSERVED WITH

European Southern Observatory

MPG/ESO 2.2-m Telescope

THOR'S HELMET

Mighty wings of gas curve back on either side of a steely-blue dome to produce the distinctive structure of NGC 2359, otherwise known as the Thor's Helmet Nebula. This emission nebula in the constellation of Canis Major lies around 15,000 light years from Earth and covers an area of space some 30 light years in diameter.

In this image from the Cerro Tololo Inter-American Observatory, stars are shown in true colour, while hydrogen and oxygen emissions are enhanced in red and blue-green respectively. The outlying reddish glows of hydrogen therefore show that the nebula is surrounded by a cloud of interstellar gas.

The central dome of Thor's Helmet reveals the reality of the forces at work in this region of space – its rippled surface is very similar to that of the Bubble Nebula (see page 118), and it has a similar cause. High-speed stellar winds from a central superhot 'Wolf-Rayet' star produce an illuminated shockwave where they plough into surrounding interstellar matter. In the case of NGC 2359, however, the situation is further complicated by the fact that the entire system is moving at high speed through the interstellar medium. As a result, a second, curving shockwave forms like the wake around a ship as the bubble ploughs into the surrounding material.

OBJECT **Thor's Helmet Nebula, NGC 2359**

DISTANCE **15,000 light years**

RA **07h 18m 30s**

DEC **-13° 13' 48"**

OBSERVED WITH

Cerro Tololo Inter-American Observatory

Prompt Telescopes

MIMAS AMONG
THE RINGS

An entrancing study in light and shadow captures the delicate relationship between Saturn, its rings and satellites. In this stunning view from NASA's Cassini spaceprobe, the small inner moon Mimas hangs above the orb of Saturn itself, at the boundary between sunlight and the shadow cast by a broad swathe of the rings. Near the bottom of the picture, the semi-transparent rings sweep across the striated sphere. The image was taken in 2004, shortly after Cassini's arrival in orbit, when Saturn's southern hemisphere was experiencing midsummer, and its north was in winter. In this image, the Cassini's cameras look up towards Saturn's northern hemisphere, past the underside of the rings. The bright band near Mimas is created by sunlight shining through the Cassini Division, a wide gap between the main A and B rings. Mimas itself is a small icy moon, with a diameter of just 396 kilometres (246 miles).

The bulk of Saturn's bluish winter hemisphere is cast into deep shadow by the B ring, with the shadows of thinner ringlets in the C and D rings appearing less dark towards the bottom of the picture. A thin wedge of the A ring (incorporating the narrow Encke Division) sweeps across the bottom of the picture, with the thread-like F ring arcing gracefully beyond it. The F ring is the outermost bright element of Saturn's ring system, but more tenuous, less sharply defined rings extend far out into the space around Saturn (see page 146).

OBJECT **Mimas**

SATELLITE OF **Saturn**

MIN DISTANCE **1.2 billion km (750 million miles)**

DIAMETER **396 km (246 miles)**

OBSERVED WITH **Cassini**
Imaging Science Subsystem

INFRARED PAW PRINT

Countless stars emerge from the darkness of interstellar dust clouds in an infrared image of the famous Cat's Paw Nebula, NGC 6334. In visible-light images (see page 128), the nebula is dominated by the pinkish gas clouds and dividing dust streams that produce its distinct resemblance to an animal's paw, but this infrared image sees through all but the densest dust to reveal the hidden heat radiation from stars within and beyond.

The view was captured by VISTA, the European Southern Observatory's Visible and Infrared Survey Telescope for Astronomy, a 4.1-metre (13.5-ft) instrument at Paranal Observatory in Chile. In the cold, arid conditions of the Atacama desert, VISTA can detect near-infrared radiation that passes straight through the intervening dust clouds but is normally absorbed by water vapour in Earth's atmosphere.

The result is a panorama filled with stars, covering an area roughly 50 light years across and 5,500 light years from Earth. Gas clouds are rendered semi-transparent to reveal the newborn stars and clusters within them, while the densest dust lanes are spotted with glowing orange patches. These orange 'hot spots' are thought to be created where escaping gas from stars that are still being formed is colliding with and heating up the surrounding nebula.

OBJECT **Cat's Paw Nebula, NGC 6334**

DISTANCE **5,500 light years**

RA **17h 19m 58s**

DEC **-35° 57' 47"**

OBSERVED WITH **European Southern Observatory**
Visible and Infrared Survey Telescope for Astronomy

MYSTIC MOUNTAIN

A collection of extraordinary twisting pinnacles rises from an outcrop of dust in the Carina Nebula, the jets blasting from their rugged peaks recalling the irresistible gaze of Tolkien's 'Eye of Sauron'. This strange landscape, understandably nicknamed Mystic Mountain by the scientists who captured it in 2010 through the Hubble Space Telescope's Wide Field Camera 3, stretches across three light years of space, some 7,500 light years from Earth. Blue colours in the image mark light emissions from oxygen, green shows hydrogen and nitrogen, while sulphurous regions appear red.

The resemblance of these spiralling towers to twisters on Earth is more than coincidental – the same laws of physics operate in the sparse gas clouds of interstellar space as in our own planet's atmosphere. The large difference in temperature between the warm outer surface of a dust-laden gas column and its cold interior can combine with pressure from starlight to produce shear forces that twist it into a tornado-like structure. A haze across the surface of the dense clouds shows where their gases are being ionized by ultraviolet starlight.

Perhaps the most impressive feature of the image, however, are the jets emerging from two of the peaks. Known as Herbig-Haro objects, these are produced where newly formed stars, still embedded in the tops of the pillars, fling out excess material from their poles into nearby space.

OBJECT **Carina Nebula, NGC 3372**

DISTANCE **7,500 light years**

RA **10h 44m 05s**

DEC **-59° 29' 45"**

OBSERVED WITH **Hubble Space Telescope**

Wide Field Camera 3

INFRARED RAINBOW

The familiar colours of visible light are a physiological response of the human eye to different wavelengths of electromagnetic radiation – the shortest visible waves appear violet, while the longest appear deep red, with a whole rainbow of colours in between. But while we naturally see all this variety in one tiny portion of the overall electromagnetic spectrum, it's easy to forget that invisible radiations have their own variations and 'colour'. This strange swirling rendition of the familiar Orion Nebula attempts to capture some of the variety in the infrared part of the spectrum, using data from two orbiting satellites and false colours to bring the differences in wavelengths within our comprehension.

The Spitzer Space Telescope is designed to observe relatively short, higher-energy infrared wavelengths – its observations of radiation at 8 and 24 micrometres (millionths of a metre) are shown in blue. The Herschel Space Observatory's observations of radiation from cooler regions, at 70 and 160 micrometres, are shown in green and red respectively. In the resulting image, the normal structure of the Orion Nebula (see page 96) disappears almost completely, but new details shine through. Most noticeable are the embryonic stars glowing amid the chaos. Locked away inside opaque cocoons of dust that hide them in visible-light observations, the range of colour among these protostars reveals that they are rapidly being heated up and cooled down, perhaps by the passage of compression waves through this turbulent region of space.

OBJECT **Orion Nebula, M42**

DISTANCE **1,500 light years**

RA **05h 35m 17s**

DEC **-05° 23' 28"**

OBSERVED WITH **Spitzer Space Telescope,**
Herschel Space Observatory

COOL CARINA

Dark dust canyons are set ablaze with unexpected fires in this stunning composite view of the enormous Carina star-forming region. The image overlays radio emissions detected by the European Southern Observatory's 12-metre (39.5-ft) APEX radio telescope onto a visible-light image from the Cerro Tololo Inter-American Observatory. Orange light corresponds to submillimetre radio waves – the shortest form of radio waves, generally produced by cold grains of interstellar dust at temperatures of around -250°C (-420°F). Luminous pink clouds, meanwhile, are produced by hydrogen fluorescing in the radiation from newborn stars. Together, therefore, the two colours map the locations of the raw materials of star formation.

The nebula contains about 165,000 times the mass of the Sun, one-sixth of which is accounted for by stars, while the remainder is gas and dust. The heart of the nebula, around the dying giant star Eta Carinae, is located at the centre of the picture, which encompasses roughly 150 light years from one side to the other.

OBJECT **Carina Nebula, NGC 3372**
DISTANCE **7,500 light years**
RA **10h 45m 09s**
DEC **-59° 52' 04"**
OBSERVED WITH
Cerro Tololo Inter-American Observatory Curtis Schmidt Telescope, Atacama Pathfinder Experiment

➤ OPPOSITE

FOMALHAUT

An extraordinary composite of visible and infrared images captures a solar system in the act of formation. The blaze of light at the centre of this image comes from Fomalhaut, a star with 2.1 times the mass of the Sun and 18 times its luminosity. This youthful star, some 25 light years from Earth, emits unusually large amounts of infrared radiation – a sign that it is surrounded by a broad disc of dust. In 2005, the Hubble Space Telescope photographed this disc directly, revealing an uncannily eye-like structure in which most of the dust is concentrated in a narrow ring, perhaps shepherded by the gravity of planets orbiting nearby.

In this composite, the Hubble image is shown in blue (apparently empty areas are artefacts of the imaging process), while a radio map from the European Southern Observatory's ALMA radio telescope is shown in orange. The sharp inner and outer edges to the ring, confirmed by the ALMA image, suggest the influence of at least two planets around Fomalhaut – one orbiting within the ring and the other outside.

OBJECT **Fomalhaut**
DISTANCE **25 light years**
RA **22h 57m 39s**
DEC **-29° 37' 20"**
OBSERVED WITH
Hubble Space Telescope Advanced Camera for Surveys, European Southern Observatory Atacama Large Millimeter Array

➤➤ OVERLEAF

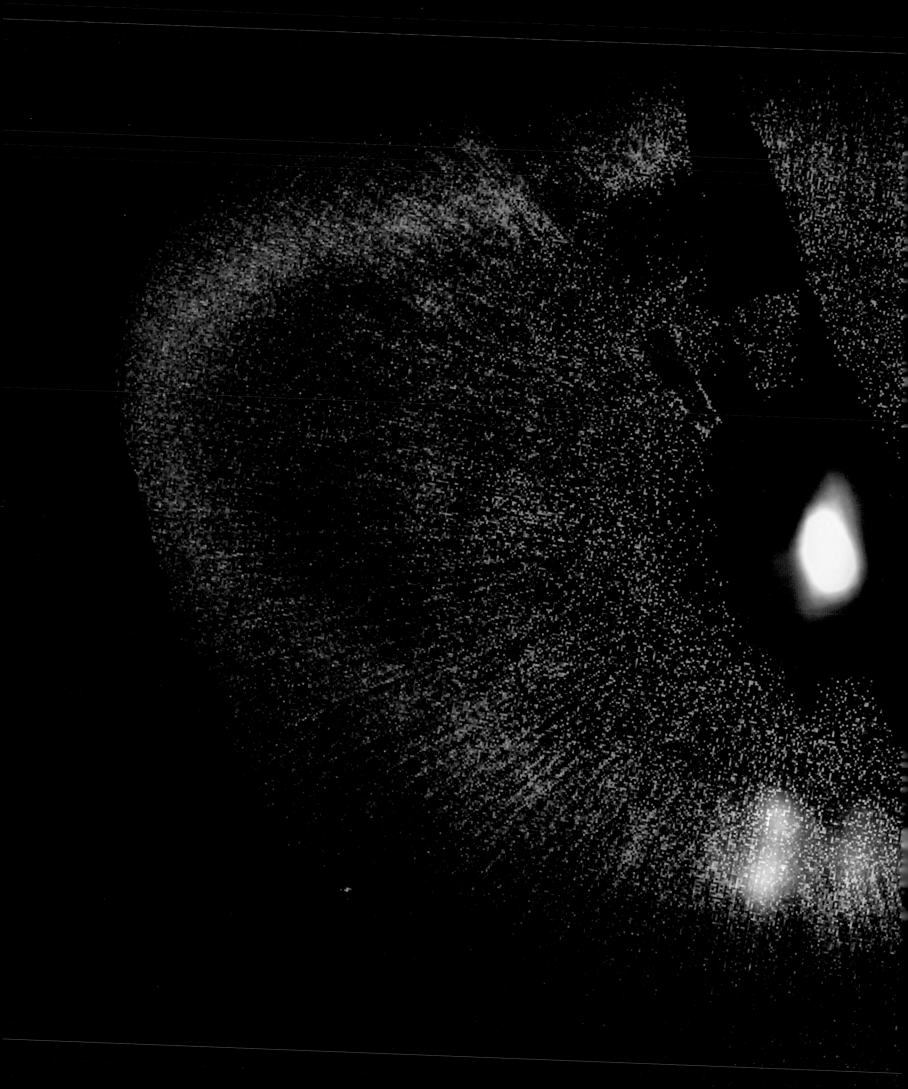

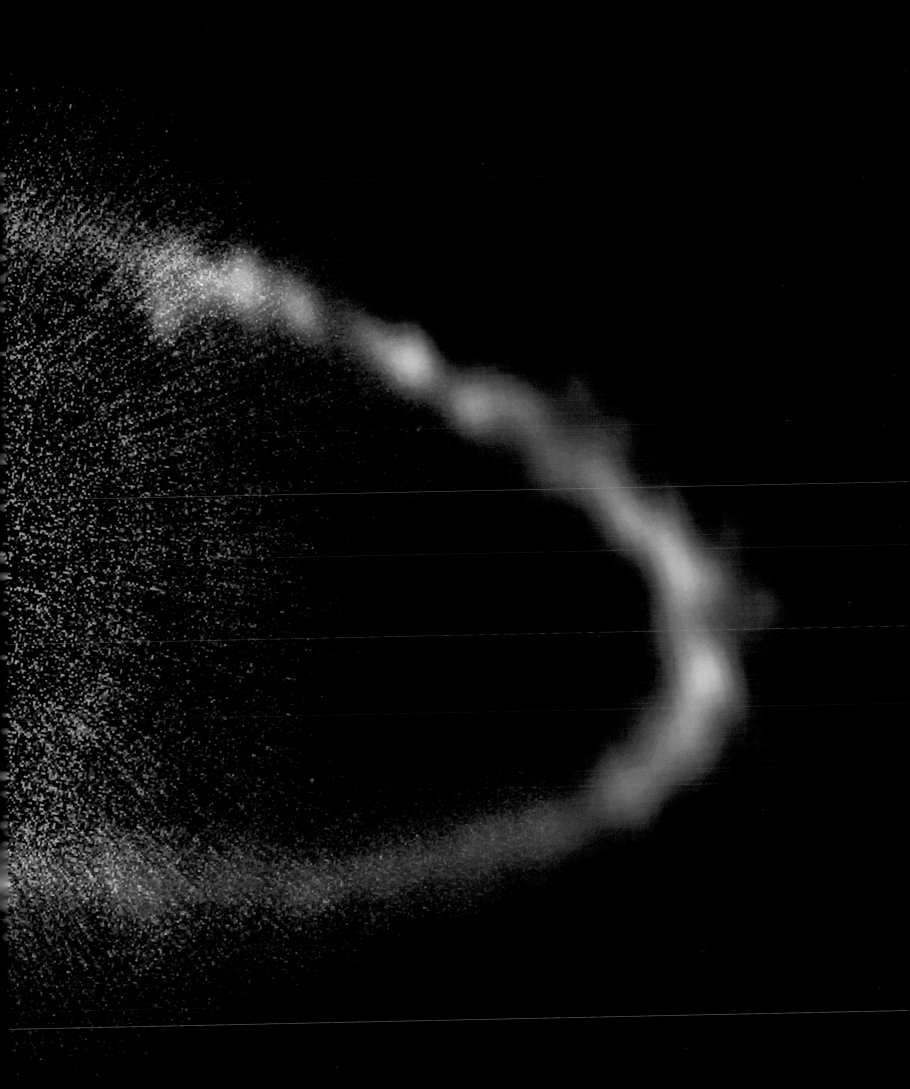

TRANSIT OF VENUS

This astonishing image captures a rare cosmic event that brings a little of the scale of the Universe home to us. On 5 June 2012, Venus passed in front of the Sun as seen from Earth, in an event known as a transit that will not happen again until 2117. The Hinode satellite, a joint project of NASA and the Japan Aerospace Exploration Agency JAXA, tracked this chance alignment from orbit, using a 'hydrogen alpha' filter to block most of the light from the Sun's dazzling disc while still retaining important details.

Venus, whose diameter of 12,104 kilometres (7,521 miles) is just 5 per cent smaller than Earth itself, lay 43 million kilometres (27 million miles) from Earth when this photograph was taken, dwarfed by the Sun some 110 million kilometres (68 million miles) beyond it. The H-alpha filter renders the Sun's surface into a seething mass of granulation, while picking up delicate features – rising pillars of flame known as spicules and looping magnetic arcs called prominences – along its limb. Venus itself, however, remains a silhouetted mystery, its circular form completed at the Sun's edge by sunlight refracted through its thick atmosphere. In past times, astronomers hoped to use the transit of Venus to learn more about its properties, but their efforts were largely frustrated – the transits of 2004 and 2012, in contrast, have been widely observed but reduced somewhat to astronomical curiosities.

OBJECT **Venus**

MIN DISTANCE **38.2 million km (23.7 million miles)**

DIAMETER **12,104 km (7,521 miles)**

OBSERVED WITH **Hinode**

Solar Optical Telescope

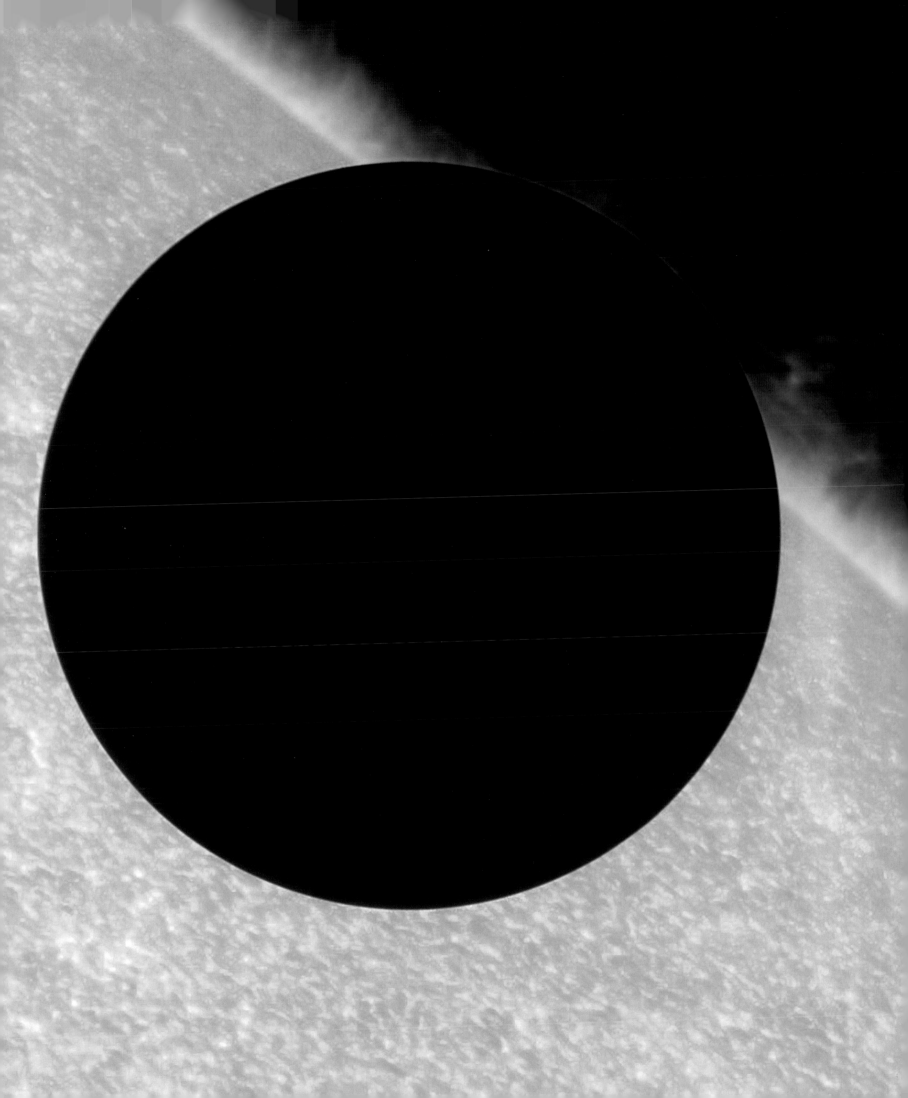

SOLAR FLARE

Loops of hot gas burst from the Sun's turbulent surface in this stunning image from NASA's Solar Dynamics Observatory (SDO), creating spots of intense heat with the power to blast high-energy particles out across the solar system.

Solar flares are among the most violent events in the solar system – enormous outbursts created when loops of magnetic field such as those shown here short-circuit and 'reconnect' closer to the Sun's surface. Tremendous amounts of energy liberated in the process heat pockets of gas to searing temperatures of up to 2 million°C (3.6 million°F), allowing them to escape the Sun's gravity completely. As particles from a solar flare (or an even more violent 'coronal mass ejection') race out across the solar system at speeds comparable to the speed of light, they interact with the magnetic fields and atmospheres of any planets they encounter, creating spectacular polar lights or aurorae.

This SDO view captures the Sun in extreme ultraviolet radiation – short-wavelength, high-energy rays only produced by its hottest regions and most violent processes. At this energy, the comparatively cool visible surface or photosphere appears dark, and SDO sees only the swirling gases of the much hotter but more tenuous outer atmosphere or corona. Loops of magnetic field, meanwhile, are picked out in detail thanks to the radiation release as charged particles spiral back and forth along them.

OBJECT **The Sun**

MEAN DISTANCE **149.6 million km (93 million miles)**

DIAMETER **1.392 million km (865,000 miles)**

OBSERVED WITH **Solar Dynamics Observatory**
Atmospheric Imaging Assembly

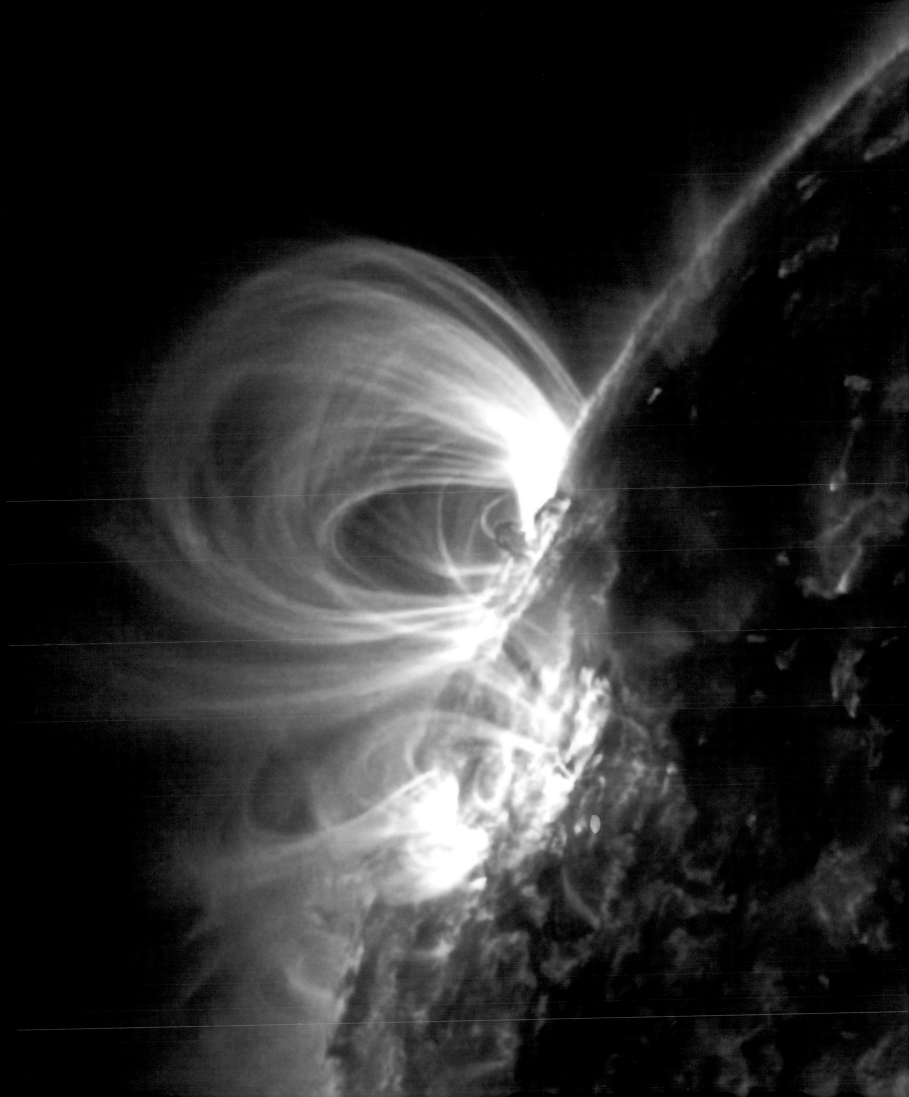

CRAB NEBULA

A web of incandescent debris from a fading stellar explosion is blasted across the sky in this beautiful Hubble Space Telescope image. In 1054, stargazers from China to North America recorded the eruption of a brilliant new star, bright enough to see in daylight, close to the horns of Taurus, the Bull. The outburst faded over many months, and was unknown to later European astronomers, but in 1731 British astronomer John Bevis stumbled across its glowing remains while compiling a star catalogue. In 1758, it was independently discovered by French astronomer Charles Messier, who made it the first entry (M1) in his list of non-stellar celestial objects. The remnant only gained its common name of the Crab Nebula after the Irish astronomer Lord Rosse made an influential sketch of it in 1844.

Today, astronomers know that the Crab is the wreckage of the 1054 explosion – an event now known as the Crab Supernova. This enormous stellar explosion marked the death of a massive, unstable star and the birth of a rapidly spinning, superdense stellar remnant called a pulsar. From Earth, the pulsar appears to flash 30 times every second as it rotates, while powerful beams of radiation and subatomic particles ejected from its poles help shape the nebula from within.

The Hubble image is a mosaic of 24 individual exposures, colour coded to show the distribution of elements within the shredded gas – green indicates sulphur, while blue and red indicate different states of oxygen.

OBJECT **Crab Nebula, M1**

DISTANCE **6,500 light years**

RA **05h 34m 32s**

DEC **+22° 00' 52"**

OBSERVED WITH **Hubble Space Telescope**

Wide Field and Planetary Camera 2

WARPED BEAUTY

Dense dust spattered with the intense pink knots of star-forming nebulae and the blue blaze of newborn star clusters define the twisted helix shape of spiral galaxy Messier 66 in this Hubble Space Telescope image. Galaxies such as M66 are defined by their spiral arms – chains of nebulae and young star clusters that stand out from the fainter background stars of the galaxy's flattened 'disc'. These slowly rotate over 100 million years or more, but they are not solid structures. Instead, they are constantly regenerated as the raw materials of star formation, in their own independent orbits around the galaxy's central hub, pass through a spiral 'compression zone' that triggers new waves of starbirth.

Messier 66, however, shows some unique features – most obviously, its spiral arms are asymmetrical, erupting out of the plane of the galaxy. In fact, one of the arms is so warped that it is disconnected from the rest of the galaxy in an independent orbit. The bright core of M66, packed with countless stars, is also distinctly 'off-centre'. Astronomers believe these distortions were caused by a close encounter with another galaxy in the relatively recent past. M66 is the brightest and largest member of the so-called 'Leo Triplet', a compact group of three spiral galaxies that also includes M65 and NGC 3628. The trajectories of M66 and NGC 3628 suggest that they are moving apart from a near-collision about a billion years ago.

OBJECT **Messier 66, NGC 3627**

DISTANCE **36 million light years**

RA **11h 20m 15s**

DEC **+12° 59' 30"**

OBSERVED WITH **Hubble Space Telescope**

Advanced Camera for Surveys

CHRISTMAS
TREE CLUSTER

A sparkling inverted triangle of newborn stars stands out against a backdrop of vibrant pink in this beautiful true-colour image from the European Southern Observatory's La Silla Observatory. The Christmas Tree Cluster, catalogued as NGC 2264, lies around 2,500 light years from Earth in the constellation of Monoceros and is scattered across roughly 30 light years of space.

First observed by German-British astronomer William Herschel in 1784, the stars of the cluster formed just a few million years ago, and as a result the brightest and most massive stars in the cluster (which naturally age and die far more rapidly than average stars like our own Sun) are still present here. The brightest of all, at the top of the picture, is in fact a tightly bound system containing multiple heavyweight stars.

The glowing nebula that forms a backdrop to the cluster is split by astronomers into several separate objects with evocative names, such as the 'Fox Fur' and 'Snowflake' nebulas. These glowing clouds of hydrogen are fluorescing thanks to the ultraviolet radiation they absorb from the cluster stars themselves. Near the bottom of the picture, the dark tower of the Cone Nebula marks a site of ongoing star formation. Infrared studies of the Cone, piercing its outer envelope of dust, have identified infant stars already glowing in its depths. Ultimately, these will be released from their cocoon to create another brilliant star cluster.

OBJECT **Christmas Tree Cluster, NGC 2264**

DISTANCE **2,500 light years**

RA **06h 40m 53s**

DEC **+09° 36' 17"**

OBSERVED WITH **European Southern Observatory**
MPG/ESO 2.2-m Telescope

A SWIRL OF STARS

A maelstrom of light looms large against a backdrop of countless more distant galaxies in this Hubble Space Telescope image. Galaxy NGC 4921 is a curious spiral star system within the Coma Cluster, a major galaxy group around 320 million light years from Earth in the constellation of Coma Berenices. This long-exposure image, a composite made by layering 80 separate exposures at visible and near-infrared wavelengths for a total exposure time of 27 hours, brings out normally unseen details of the galaxy's hazy disc. In normal spirals, the light of the disc is drowned out by the presence of brilliant open star clusters and star-formation regions that define the spiral's arms (see, for instance, the Whirlpool Galaxy, page 98).

NGC 4921, however, is an 'anaemic' spiral, with very weak spiral arms that are traceable mostly through dark silhouetted dust lanes and bright blue star clusters above and to the right of the central hub. In this case, the long exposure brings out more detail in the disc, where the galaxy's slow-living, Sun-like stars mostly reside.

According to accepted theories, spiral arm formation is intensified by interactions with other galaxies, and so we might expect to see weak spiral arms in an isolated and remote galaxy. Finding such a poorly defined spiral in the heart of the Coma Cluster – a group of around a thousand members where close galactic encounters are common – is therefore something of a puzzle.

OBJECT **NGC 4921**

DISTANCE **320 million light years**

RA **12h 59m 02s**

DEC **+28° 09' 17"**

OBSERVED WITH **Hubble Space Telescope**

Advanced Camera for Surveys

MOUNTAIN GIANTS

A cluster of brilliant stars emerges from the clouds above a craggy celestial outcrop in this glorious cosmic landscape from the Hubble Space Telescope. The star cluster, known as Pismis 24, lies more than 8,000 light years from Earth in the constellation of Scorpius, and is the product of recent star formation in the nearby nebula NGC 6357. Particles from the stellar winds of Pismis 24 bombard the outer surface of the nebula, carving its dense clouds into a series of peaks.

The brightest star in the cluster, known as Pismis 24-1, was until recently a candidate for the heaviest single star in the Milky Way, with the apparent weight of 300 Suns. However, astronomers were doubtful about whether such a stellar monster could physically hold itself together through the trials of its creation, so they used Hubble's crystal-clear vision to take a closer look. The results confirmed that this giant is actually a multiple system, containing at least two – and perhaps three – stars. This reduces the maximum weight of each star in the system to a more manageable 100 Suns.

OBJECT **Pismis 24, NGC 6357**

DISTANCE **8,150 light years**

RA **17h 24m 43s**

DEC **-34° 11′ 57″**

OBSERVED WITH

Hubble Space Telescope

Advanced Camera for Surveys

➤ OPPOSITE

AROUND A
MONSTER STAR

Intense radiation from the brilliant star WR22 generates a web of light and shadow around the edges of the Carina Nebula, some 7,500 light years from Earth. WR22, seen at the centre of the image, is a rare 'Wolf-Rayet' star – a stellar monster shining so brightly that particles are blown off from its outer layers at a tremendous rate. While most stars retain nearly all of their matter from formation until the very last stages of their evolution, Wolf-Rayets lose a substantial proportion of their mass throughout their lives, and this substantially affects their development. As the cooler outer layers are blown away into space, hotter material from the interior is exposed directly at the surface, increasing the strength of the star's radiation and the rate of mass loss.

A star such as WR22, which has an estimated 77 times the mass of the Sun, may already have lost several solar masses of material. As radiation from the star pours into the surrounding nebula, it excites nearby hydrogen clouds and causes them to fluoresce in distinctive pink tones, silhouetting interstellar dust that would otherwise be invisible.

OBJECT **Carina Nebula, NGC 3372**

DISTANCE **7,500 light years**

RA **10h 41m 28s**

DEC **-59° 40′ 17″**

OBSERVED WITH

European Southern Observatory

MPG/ESO 2.2-m Telescope

➤ ➤ OVERLEAF

GLOSSARY

Active galaxy
A galaxy that emits large amounts of energy from its central regions, probably generated as matter falls into a supermassive black hole at the heart of the galaxy.

Asteroid
One of the countless rocky worlds of the inner solar system, largely confined in the main Asteroid Belt beyond the orbit of Mars.

Astronomical unit
A unit of measurement widely used in astronomy, equivalent to Earth's average distance from the Sun – roughly 150 million kilometres (93 million miles).

Atom
A basic building block of matter consisting of a central positively charged nucleus orbited by one or more negatively charged electrons, resulting in an overall neutral electric charge. The precise number of subatomic particles within an atom determines which element it forms. Atoms join together to form molecules, and when they display an electric charge (usually from the loss or addition of electrons) they form ions.

Atmosphere
A shell of gases held around a planet or star by its gravity.

Barred spiral galaxy
A spiral galaxy in which the arms are linked to the hub by a straight bar of stars and other material.

Binary star
A pair of stars in orbit around one another. Because the stars in a binary pair were usually born at the same time, they allow a direct comparison of the way that stars with different properties evolve.

Black hole
A superdense point in space, usually formed by a collapsing stellar core more than five times the mass of the Sun. A black hole's gravity is so powerful that even light cannot escape from it.

Brown dwarf
A so-called 'failed star' that never gains enough mass to begin the fusion of hydrogen in its core, and so never starts to shine properly. Instead, brown dwarfs radiate low-energy radiation (mostly infrared) through gravitational contraction and a more limited form of fusion.

Comet
A chunk of rock and ice from the outer reaches of the Solar System. When comets fall into orbits that bring them close to the Sun, they heat up and their surface ices evaporate, forming a coma and a tail.

Cryovolcanism
A strange form of geological activity found on some of the icy moons of the outer solar system. Cryovolcanism typically involves eruptions of runny ice, kept 'molten' by the presence of significant amounts of ammonia.

Dark nebula
A cloud of interstellar gas and dust that absorbs light, and only becomes visible when silhouetted against a field of stars or other nebulae.

DEC (Declination)
A celestial co-ordinate measurement roughly analogous to latitude on Earth's surface, used in conjunction with Right Ascension.

Dwarf planet
Any object that is in an independent orbit around the Sun, and has sufficient gravity to pull itself into a roughly spherical shape, but which, unlike a true planet, has not cleared the region around it of other objects.

Eclipse
See solar eclipse, lunar eclipse.

Electromagnetic radiation
A form of energy consisting of combined electric and magnetic waves, able to propagate itself across a vacuum at the speed of light. The energy or temperature of an object emitting radiation affects its wavelength and other characteristics.

Electron
One of the elementary particles of the Universe, with negative electric charge and very small mass, usually found orbiting around the central nucleus of an atom.

Elliptical galaxy
A galaxy consisting of stars in orbits that have no particular orientation, and generally lacking in star-forming gas. Ellipticals are among the smallest and largest galaxies known.

Emission nebula
A cloud of gas in space that glows at very specific wavelengths, producing a spectrum full of 'emission lines'. These nebulae are usually energized by the high-energy light of nearby stars, and are often associated with star-formation regions.

Flare
A huge release of superheated particles above the surface of a star, caused by a short circuit in its magnetic field.

Galaxy
An independent system of stars, gas and other material with a size measured in thousands of light years.

Gamma rays
The highest-energy forms of electromagnetic radiation, with extremely short wavelengths, generated by the hottest objects and most energetic processes in the Universe.

Giant planet
A planet comprising a huge envelope of gas, liquid, or slushy ice (various frozen chemicals), perhaps around a relatively small rocky core.

Globular cluster
A dense ball of ancient, long-lived stars, in orbit around a galaxy such as the Milky Way.

Infrared
Electromagnetic radiation with slightly less energy than visible light. Infrared radiation is typically emitted by warm objects too cool to glow visibly.

Ionization
A process by which an atom is transformed into an electrically charged form known as an ion, usually by the injection of energy (for instance from ultraviolet radiation) that allows one of its electrons to escape.

Irregular galaxy
A galaxy with no obvious structure, generally rich in gas, dust, and star-forming regions.

Kuiper Belt
A doughnut-shaped ring of icy worlds directly beyond the orbit of Neptune. The largest known Kuiper Belt Objects are Pluto and Eris.

Light year
A common unit of astronomical measurement, equivalent to the distance travelled by light (or other electromagnetic radiation) in one year. A light year is equivalent to roughly 9.5 million million kilometres (5.9 trillion miles).

Luminosity
A measure of the energy output of a star. Although luminosity is technically measured in watts, the stars are so luminous that it is simpler to compare them with the Sun. A star's visual luminosity (the energy it produces in visible light) is not necessarily equivalent to its overall luminosity in all radiations.

Lunar eclipse
An event during which the Full Moon passes through Earth's shadow and is blocked from the illumination of direct sunlight.

Main sequence
A term used to describe the longest phase in a star's life, during which it is relatively stable, and shines by fusing hydrogen into helium at its core. During this period, the star obeys a general relationship that links its mass, size, luminosity and colour.

Multiple star
A system of two or more stars in orbit around one another (pairs of stars are also called binaries). Most of the stars in

Nebula
Any cloud of gas or dust floating in space. Nebulae are the material from which stars are born, and into which they are scattered again at the end of their lives. The word means cloud in Latin and was originally applied to any fuzzy object in the sky, including some we now know to be star clusters or distant galaxies

Neutron star
The collapsed core of a supermassive star, left behind by a supernova explosion. A neutron star consists of compressed subatomic particles, and is the densest known object - though in the most massive stars, the core can collapse past the neutron star stage to form a black hole. Many neutron stars initially behave as pulsars.

Nova
A binary star system in which a white dwarf is pulling material from a companion star, building up a layer of gas around itself that then burns away in a violent nuclear explosion.

Nuclear fusion
The joining-together of light atomic nuclei (the central cores of atoms) to make heavier ones at very high temperatures and pressures, releasing excess energy in the process. Fusion is the process by which the stars shine.

Oort Cloud
A spherical shell of dormant comets, up to two light years across, surrounding the entire solar system.

Open cluster
A large group of bright young stars that have recently been born from the same star-forming nebula, and may still be embedded in its gas clouds.

Planet
A world that follows its own orbit around the Sun, is massive enough to pull itself into a spherical shape, and which has cleared the space around it of other objects (apart from satellites). According to this definition, there are eight planets – Mercury, Venus, Earth, Mars, Jupiter, Saturn, Uranus and Neptune.

Planetary nebula
An expanding cloud of glowing gas sloughed off from the outer layers of a dying red giant star as it transforms into a white dwarf.

Protostar
A star that is still coalescing from the collapse of a gas cloud under its own gravity. As the centre of the cloud heats up, it may emit infrared radiation.

Pulsar
A rapidly spinning neutron star with an intense magnetic field that channels its radiation out along two narrow beams that sweep across the sky.

RA (Right Ascension)
A celestial co-ordinate measurement roughly analogous to longitude on Earth's surface, used in conjunction with Declination.

Radio waves
The lowest-energy form of electromagnetic radiation, with the longest wavelengths. Radio waves are emitted by cool gas clouds in space, but also by violent active galaxies and pulsars.

Radar
A technique useful both in tracking objects such as aircraft and in mapping planetary surfaces. Radar (an acronym for Radio Detection and Ranging) involves sending a beam of radio waves towards a target and measuring the time for the echo to return in order to calculate the target's precise distance.

Red dwarf
A star with considerably less mass than the Sun - small, faint, and with a low surface temperature. Red dwarfs fuse hydrogen into helium in their cores very slowly, and live for much longer than the Sun, despite their size.

Red giant
A star passing through a phase of its life where its luminosity has increased hugely, causing its outer layers to expand and its surface to cool. Stars usually enter red giant phases when they exhaust the fuel supplies in their core.

Reflection nebula
A cloud of interstellar gas and dust that shines as it reflects or scatters light from nearby stars.

Rocky planet
A relatively small planet composed largely of rocks and minerals, perhaps with a thin envelope of gas and liquid.

Solar eclipse
A rare event during which the Moon passes directly across the face of the Sun, casting its shadow onto the surface of the Earth. The alignment must be so precise that a dramatic total eclipse is usually only visible in a narrow band across Earth's surface, but partial eclipses can be seen far more widely.

Spectral lines
Dark or light bands in a spectrum of light that correspond to certain wavelengths. Bright emission lines can indicate that an object is emitting certain wavelengths, while dark bands silhouetted against a broad background spectrum indicate that something is absorbing the light on its way to us. In both cases, the location of the lines offers information on which atoms or molecules are involved.

Spectrum
The spread-out band of light created by passing light through a prism or similar device. The prism bends light by different amounts depending on its wavelength and colour, so the spectrum reveals the precise intensities of light at different wavelengths.

Spiral galaxy
A galaxy consisting of a hub of old yellow stars, surrounded by a flattened disk of younger stars, gas and dust, with spiral arms marking regions of current star formation.

Star
A dense ball of gas that has collapsed into a spherical shape and become hot and dense enough at its centre to trigger nuclear fusion reactions that make it luminous.

Stellar wind
A stream of high-energy particles blasted off the surface of a star by the pressure of its radiation, and spreading across the surrounding space.

Sun
The star at the centre of Earth's solar system. The Sun is a fairly average low-mass star, and a useful comparison for other stars. Its key properties include a diameter of 1.39 million kilometres (865,000 miles), a mass of 2,000 trillion trillion tonnes, energy output of 380 trillion trillion watts, and a surface temperature of 5,500°C (9,900°F).

Sun-like star
A yellow star with roughly the same mass, luminosity and surface temperature as the Sun. Stars like this are of particular interest to astronomers because they are long-lived and stable, so any planets around them are potential havens for life.

Supergiant
A massive and extremely luminous star with between 10 and 70 times the mass of the Sun. Supergiants can have almost any colour, depending on how the balance of their energy output and their size affects their surface temperature.

Supermassive black hole
A black hole with the mass of millions of stars, believed to lie in the very centre of many galaxies. Supermassive black holes form from the collapse of huge gas clouds rather than the death of massive stars.

Supernova
A cataclysmic explosion marking the death of a star. Supernovae can be triggered when a heavyweight star exhausts the last of its fuel and its core collapses (forming either a neutron star or a black hole) or when a white dwarf in a nova system tips over its upper mass limit and collapses suddenly into a neutron star.

Supernova remnant
A cloud of superheated gas expanding from the site of a former supernova explosion.

Transit
The passage of one celestial body across the face of another, such as the movement of a planet across the face of a star.

Ultraviolet
Electromagnetic radiation with wavelengths slightly shorter than visible light, typically radiated by objects hotter than the Sun. The hottest stars give out much of their energy as ultraviolet radiation.

Variable star
A star that varies its brightness, either due to interaction with another star, or because of some feature of the star itself (most commonly a pulsation in size that may be periodic or irregular).

Visible light
Electromagnetic radiation with wavelengths between 400 and 700 nanometres (billionths of a metre), corresponding to the sensitivity of the human eye. Stars like the Sun emit most of their energy in the form of visible light.

White dwarf
A stellar remnant left behind by the death of a star with less than about eight times the Sun's mass. White dwarfs are dense, slowly cooling stellar cores – very hot, but faint on account of their tiny size.

Wolf-Rayet star
A star with extremely high mass that develops such fierce stellar winds that it blows away most of its outer layers in a few million years, exposing the extremely hot interior.

X-rays
High-energy electromagnetic radiation emitted by extremely hot objects and violent processes in the Universe. Material heated as it is pulled towards a black hole is one of the strongest sources of astronomical X-rays.

ACKNOWLEDGEMENTS

2: NASA/JPL/Space Science Institute; 4: Credit: NASA, ESA, HEIC, and The Hubble Heritage Team (STScI/AURA). Acknowledgment: R. Corradi (Isaac Newton Group of Telescopes, Spain) and Z. Tsvetanov (NASA); 6–7: R. Richins, enchantedskies.net; 8–9: NASA/ESA and The Hubble Heritage Team STScI/AURA); 10–11: ESO/T. Preibisch; 12(l–r): NASA, ESA, and the Hubble Heritage Team (STScI/AURA) - ESA/Hubble Collaboration; NASA/JPL/University of Arizona; NASA, ESA, the Hubble Heritage (STScI/AURA)-ESA/Hubble Collaboration, and W. Keel (University of Alabama); NASA, ESA, and the Hubble SM4 ERO Team; 15: BABAK TAFRESHI, TWAN/SCIENCE PHOTO LIBRARY; 17: NASA/Johns Hopkins University Applied Physics Laboratory/Carnegie Institution of Washington; 19: NASA/JPL-Caltech/USGS; 21: NASA, ESA, and the Hubble Heritage Team (STScI/AURA) - ESA/Hubble Collaboration; 23: Hubble Heritage Team (AURA/STScI/NASA); 25: ESA/Hubble & NASA; 27: ESO/J. Emerson/VISTA. Acknowledgment: Cambridge Astronomical Survey Unit; 28–29: NASA/JPL/University of Arizona; 31: ESO/APEX (MPIfR/ESO/OSO)/T. Stanke et al./Igor Chekalin/Digitized Sky Survey 2; 33: NASA, ESA, the Hubble Heritage (STScI/AURA)-ESA/Hubble Collaboration, and W. Keel (University of Alabama); 35: NASA/JPL/University of Arizona; 37: ESA/Hubble & NASA; 39: NASA/JPL/Space Science Institute; 41: NASA, ESA, and the Hubble SM4 ERO Team; 43: ESO/S. Brunier; 45: X-ray: NASA/CXC/SAO/J.DePasquale; IR: NASA/JPL-Caltech; Optical: NASA/STScI; 46–47: Credit: NASA, ESA, and The Hubble Heritage Team (STScI/AURA); 48 (l–r): NASA/JPL-Caltech/Space Science Institute; NASA/JPL/Space Science Institute; NASA, ESA, and The Hubble Heritage (STScI/AURA)-ESA/Hubble Collaboration; NASA, ESA, and M. Livio (STScI); 51: NASA/Johns Hopkins University Applied Physics Laboratory/Carnegie Institution of Washington; 53: NASA/JPL/USGS; 55: NASA, ESA and J. Hester (ASU); 57: NASA/JPL-Caltech/Space Science Institute; 59: NASA/JPL-Caltech/UA; 60–61: NASA/JPL-Caltech/Space Science Institute; 63: NASA/JPL; 65: NASA, ESA, N. Smith (University of California, Berkeley), and The Hubble Heritage Team (STScI/AURA); 67: Credit: NASA, ESA, and the Hubble Heritage (STScI/AURA)-ESA/Hubble Collaboration. Acknowledgment: R. Chandar (University of Toledo) and J. Miller (University of Michigan); 69: ESA ©2009 MPS for OSIRIS Team MPS/UPD/LAM/IAA/RSSD/INTA/UPM/DASP/IDA; 71: NASA/

JPL-Caltech/UA; 73: Credit: NASA, ESA, and the Hubble Heritage (STScI/AURA)-ESA/Hubble Collaboration. Acknowledgment: J. Maíz Apellániz (Institute of Astrophysics of Andalucía, Spain); 75: NASA/JPL/USGS; 76–77: Credit: NASA, JPL; Digital processing: Björn Jónsson (IAAA); 79: NASA, ESA, and M. Livio (STScI); 81: NASA/JPL/Space Science Institute; 82 (l–r): NASA/JPL/USGS; R. Richins, enchantedskies.net; NASA/JPL-Caltech/Univ. of Arizona; N.A.Sharp, NOAO/NSO/Kitt Peak FTS/AURA/NSF; 85: NASA/JPL/Space Science Institute; 87: NASA/JPL-Caltech/Univ. of Arizona; 88–89: T. A. Rector/University of Alaska Anchorage and WIYN/NOAO/AURA/NSF; 91: NASA/JPL/USGS; 93: JERRY SCHAD/SCIENCE PHOTO LIBRARY; 95: N.A.Sharp, NOAO/NSO/Kitt Peak FTS/AURA/NSF; 97: NASA, ESA, M. Robberto (Space Telescope Science Institute/ESA) and the Hubble Space Telescope Orion Treasury Project Team; 99: NASA, ESA, S. Beckwith (STScI), and The Hubble Heritage Team (STScI/AURA); 101: ESO/J. Emerson/VISTA. Acknowledgment: Cambridge Astronomical Survey Unit; 102–103: ESO/T. Preibisch; 105: ESO/IDA/Danish 1.5 m/R. Gendler and J.-E. Ovaldsen; 107: NASA/JPL/Space Science Institute; 109: NASA, ESA, and The Hubble Heritage Team (STScI/AURA); 111: NASA, ESA, and the Hubble Heritage (STScI/AURA)-ESA/Hubble Collaboration. Acknowledgment: R. O'Connell (University of Virginia) and the WFC3 Scientific Oversight Committee; 112–113: R. Richins, enchantedskies.net; 114 (l–r): ESO/WFI (Optical); MPIfR/ESO/APEX/A.Weiss et al. (Submillimetre); NASA/CXC/CfA/R.Kraft et al. (X-ray); T.A. Rector/University of Alaska Anchorage, H. Schweiker/WIYN and NOAO/AURA/NSF; NASA/JPL/Space Science Institute; ESO; 117: NASA, ESA, C.R. O'Dell (Vanderbilt University), and M. Meixner, P. McCullough, and G. Bacon (Space Telescope Science Institute); 119: T.A. Rector/University of Alaska Anchorage, H. Schweiker/WIYN and NOAO/AURA/NSF; 121: ESO/J. Emerson/VISTA Acknowledgment: Cambridge Astronomical Survey Unit. ; 123: NASA, ESA; 125: NASA/JPL-Caltech/ASU; 127: NASA, ESA and A. Nota (STScI/ESA); 129: ESO; 130–131: NASA, ESA, SSC, CXC and STScI; 133: ESO; 135: NASA, ESA, HEIC, and The Hubble Heritage Team (STScI/AURA); 137: T.A.Rector (NRAO/AUI/NSF and NOAO/AURA/NSF) and B.A.Wolpa (NOAO/AURA/NSF); 139: ESO/WFI (Optical); MPIfR/ESO/APEX/A.Weiss et al. (Submillimetre); NASA/CXC/CfA/R.Kraft et al. (X-ray); 141: NASA/JPL/

Space Science Institute; 143: NASA/JPL-Caltech/Harvard-Smithsonian CfA; 145: NASA, ESA and The Hubble Heritage Team (STScI/AURA); 147: ESO; 148–149: NASA/JPL/Space Science Institute; 150 (l–r): NASA/JPL-Caltech/ASU; ESA/DLR/FU Berlin (G. Neukum); NASA, ESA, and the Hubble SM4 ERO Team; SDO/AIA; 153: NASA/JPL/USGS; 155: Bill Livingston/NSO/AURA/NSF ; 157: NASA, ESA, and the Hubble SM4 ERO Team; 159: NASA/JPL/USGS; 161: NASA/JPL/DLR; 162–163: ESA/DLR/FU Berlin (G. Neukum); 165: SDO/AIA; 167: NASA/JPL/ASI/ESA/Univ. of Rome/MOLA Science Team/USGS; 169: NASA/JPL/Space Science Institute; 171: ESA/DLR/FU Berlin (G. Neukum); 173: Royal Swedish Academy of Sciences (Observations: Göran Scharmer and Kai Langhans, ISP,Image processing: Mats Löfdahl, ISP); 175: NASA/JPL-Caltech/ASU; 177: ESA/NASA/JPL/University of Arizona; 179: NASA/JPL/Space Science Institute; 181: NASA, ESA, and the Hubble SM4 ERO Team; 182 (l–r): ESO/APEX/T. Preibisch et al. (Submillimetre); N. Smith, University of Minnesota/NOAO/AURA/NSF (Optical); NASA, ESA, J. Hester and A. Loll (Arizona State University); NASA SDO/AIA; NASA, ESA and Jesús Maíz Apellániz (Instituto de Astrofísica de Andalucía, Spain). Acknowledgement: Davide De Martin (ESA/Hubble); 185: ESO; 187: SSRO/PROMPT/CTIO; 189: NASA/JPL/Space Science Institute; 191: ESO/J. Emerson/VISTA. Acknowledgment: Cambridge Astronomical Survey Unit; 193: NASA, ESA, and M. Livio and the Hubble 20th Anniversary Team (STScI); 195: ESA/NASA/JPL-Caltech/N. Billot (IRAM); 197: ESO/APEX/T. Preibisch et al. (Submillimetre); N. Smith, University of Minnesota/NOAO/AURA/NSF (Optical); 198–199: ALMA (ESO/NAOJ/NRAO). Visible light image: the NASA/ESA Hubble Space Telescope; 201: JAXA/NASA/Lockheed Martin ; 203: NASA SDO/AIA; 205: NASA, ESA, J. Hester and A. Loll (Arizona State University); 207: Image credit: NASA, ESA and the Hubble Heritage (STScI/AURA)-ESA/Hubble Collaboration. Acknowledgement: Davide De Martin and Robert Gendler; 209: ESO; 211: NASA, ESA and K. Cook (Lawrence Livermore National Laboratory, USA); 213: NASA, ESA and Jesús Maíz Apellániz (Instituto de Astrofísica de Andalucía, Spain). Acknowledgement: Davide De Martin (ESA/Hubble); 214–215: ESO.

Quercus Editions Ltd
55 Baker Street
7th floor, South Block
London
W1U 8EW

First published in 2013

Copyright © 2013 Quercus Editions Ltd

A catalogue record of this book is available from the
British Library

UK and associated territories: ISBN 978 1 78087 811 9

Design and editorial by Pikaia Imaging

Printed and bound in China

10 9 8 7 6 5 4 3 2 1